Core Decodable Takehomes

Level 1 Book 2

Core Decodables 66–115

Mc Graw Hill **SRA**

Columbus, OH

SRAonline.com

 SRA

Send all inquiries to this address:
SRA/McGraw-Hill
4400 Easton Commons
Columbus, OH 43219-6188

ISBN: 978-0-07-610699-8
MHID: 0-07-610699-3

7 8 9 QWE 14 13 12 11 10

The McGraw-Hill Companies

Contents

About the Decodable Takehomes

The **SRA Imagine It!** *Decodable Takehomes* allow your students to apply their knowledge of phonic elements to read simple, engaging texts. Each story supports instruction in a new phonic element and incorporates elements and words that have been learned earlier.

The students can fold and staple the pages of each *Decodable Takehome* to make books of their own to keep and read. We suggest that you keep extra sets of the stories in your classroom for the children to reread.

How to make a Takehome

1. Tear out the pages you need.

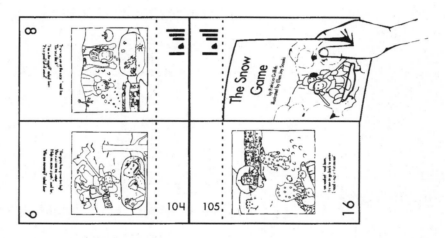

2. Place pages 4 and 5, and pages 2 and 7 faceup.

For 16-page book

3. Place the pages on top of each other in this order: pages 8 and 9, pages 6 and 11, pages 4 and 13, and pages 2 and 15.

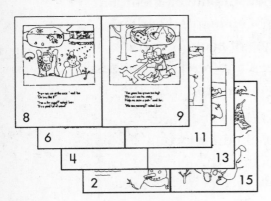

4. Fold along the center line.

5. Check to make sure the pages are in order.

6. Staple the pages along the fold.

For 8-page book

3. Place pages 4 and 5 on top of pages 2 and 7.

4. Fold along the center line.

5. Check to make sure the pages are in order.

6. Staple the pages along the fold.

Just to let you know...

A message from _____

Help your child discover the joy of independent reading with **SRA Imagine It!** From time to time your child will bring home his or her very own *Pre-Decodable* or *Decodable Takehomes* to share with you. With your help, these stories can give your child important reading practice and a joyful shared reading experience.

You may want to set aside a few minutes every evening to read these stories together. Here are some suggestions you may find helpful:

- Do not expect your child to read each story perfectly, but concentrate on sharing the book together.
- Participate by doing some of the reading.
- Talk about the stories as you read, give lots of encouragement, and watch as your child becomes more fluent throughout the year!

Learning to read takes lots of practice. Sharing these stories is one way that your child can gain that valuable practice. Encourage your child to keep the *Pre-Decodable* or *Decodable Takehomes* in a special place. This collection will make a library of books that your child can read and reread. Take the time to listen to your child read from his or her library. Just a few moments of shared reading each day can give your child the confidence needed to excel in reading.

Children who read every day come to think of reading as a pleasant, natural part of life. One way to inspire your child to read is to show that reading is an important part of your life by letting him or her see you reading books, magazines, newspapers, or any other materials. Another good way to show that you value reading is to share a *Pre-Decodable* or *Decodable Takehome* with your child each day.

Successful reading experiences allow children to be proud of their newfound reading ability. Support your child with interest and enthusiasm about reading. You won't regret it!

Previously Introduced High-Frequency Words

a	boy	from	I	now	sleep	was
about	brown	get	if	of	some	water
after	but	girl	in	old	take	way
all	by	go	into	on	that	we
am	call	going	is	one	the	well
an	came	good	it	or	their	went
and	can	got	its	out	them	were
any	come	green	jump	over	then	what
are	could	had	just	pretty	there	when
around	day	has	know	put	they	where
as	did	have	like	red	this	will
ask	do	he	little	ride	to	with
at	don't	help	long	right	too	would
away	down	her	look	said	two	yellow
be	every	here	make	saw	up	yes
before	five	him	me	see	very	you
big	for	his	my	she	walk	your
blue	four	how	no	six	want	

Sound/Spelling Correspondences in Core Decodables

1. Pre-decodable
2. Pre-decodable
3. Pre-decodable
4. Pre-decodable
5. Pre-decodable
6. /s/ spelled *s*, /m/ spelled *m*, /a/ spelled *a*
7. /t/ spelled *t, tt*
8. Review
9. /d/ spelled *d*
10. /n/ spelled *n*
11. /i/ spelled *i*
12. /h/ spelled *h_*
13. Review
14. /p/ spelled *p*
15. /l/ spelled *l, ll*
16. /o/ spelled *o*
17. /b/ spelled *b*
18. Review
19. /k/ spelled *c*
20. /aw/ spelled *al, all*
21. /k/ spelled *k*, ■*ck*
22. /r/ spelled *r*
23. /f/ spelled *f, ff*
24. /s/ spelled *ss*
25. Review
26. /g/ spelled *g*
27. /j/ spelled *j*, ■*dge*
28. /u/ spelled *u*
29. /z/ spelled *z, zz*
30. /z/ spelled *_s*

31. Review
32. /ks/ spelled ■*x*
33. /e/ spelled *e*
34. -ed ending: /ed/, /d/
35. -ed ending: /t/
36. /e/ spelled *_ea_*
37. Review
38. /sh/ spelled *sh*
39. /th/ spelled *th*
40. /ch/ spelled *ch*, ■*tch*
41. /or/ spelled *or, ore*
42. Review
43. /ar/ spelled *ar*
44. /m/ spelled *_mb*
45. /w/ spelled *w_*
46. /hw/ spelled *wh_*
47. /er/ spelled *er, ir*
48. /er/ spelled *ur*
49. Review
50. Schwa
51. Review schwa
52. /ng/ spelled ■*ng*
53. /nk/ spelled ■*nk*
54. /kw/ spelled *qu_*
55. Review
56. /y/ spelled *y_*
57. /v/ spelled *v*
58. Syllable -le
59. /ā/ spelled *a* and *a_e*
60. Review
61. /ī/ spelled *i* and *i_e*
62. /s/ spelled *ce, ci_*

63. /j/ spelled *ge, gi_*
64. Review
65. /ō/ spelled *o* and *o_e*
66. /ū/ spelled *u* and *u_e*
67. Review
68. /ē/ spelled *e* and *e_e*
69. /ē/ spelled *ee* and *ea*
70. Review
71. /ē/ spelled *_y, _ie_*
72. /s/ spelled *cy*
73. Review /s/ spellings
74. Review
75. /ā/ spelled *ai_, _ay*
76. /ī/ spelled *_igh*
77. /ī/ spelled *_ie* and *_y*
78. Review
79. /ō/ spelled *oa_, _ow*
80. /ū/ spelled *_ew* and *_ue*
81. Review
82. /ōō/ spelled *oo*
83. /ōō/ spelled *_ue* and *u*
84. Review
85. /ōō/ spelled *_ew* and *u_e*
86. /oo/ spelled *oo*
87. Review
88. /ow/ spelled *ow*
89. /ow/ spelled *ou_*
90. /n/ spelled *kn_*
91. Review

92. /aw/ spelled *au_, aw*
93. /aw/ spelled *augh, ough*
94. Review
95. /oi/ spelled *oi, _oy*
96. /r/ spelled *wr_*
97. /f/ spelled *ph*
98. Review
99. /er/ spelled *ear*
100. /ē/ spelled *_ey*
101. Review
102. Review /a/ and /ā/
103. Review /i/ and /ī/
104. Review /o/ and /ō/
105. Review /u/ and /ū/
106. Review long vowels
107. Review /e/ and /ē/
108. Review consonant blends
109. Review consonant digraphs
110. Review r-controlled vowels
111. Review
112. Review /ōō/ and /oo/
113. Review diphthongs
114. Review word endings
115. Review

SRA Decodables

Muse the Mule

by Dottie Raymer
illustrated by Jan Pyk

Core Decodable 66

 SRA

Columbus, OH

9

Muse did not like big branches on his back.
But Muse liked Hugo's music.

8

SRAonline.com

SRA

Copyright © 2008 by SRA/McGraw-Hill.

All rights reserved. The contents, or parts thereof, may be reproduced in print form for non-profit educational use with *Imagine It!* provided such reproductions bear copyright notice, but may not be reproduced in any form for any other purpose without the prior written consent of The McGraw-Hill Companies, Inc., including, but not limited to, network storage or transmission, or broadcast for distance learning. An Open Court Curriculum.

Printed in the United States of America.

Send all inquiries to this address:
SRA/McGraw-Hill
4400 Easton Commons
Columbus, OH 43219

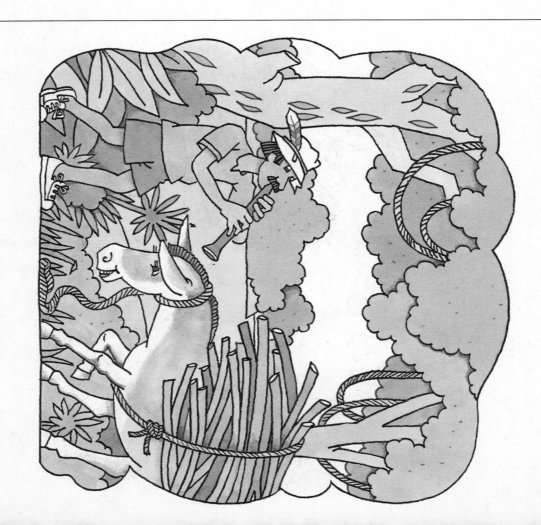

At last, Hugo played music for Muse.

Muse is a cute mule.
Muse had a forest home.

Muse did not like branches on his back.
Muse did not budge.

Muse liked the forest.
But Muse liked music the most.

Hugo cut branches and traded them.
Muse had to lug the branches on his back.

SRA Decodables

A Better Mule

by Tom Sato
illustrated by Rusty Fletcher

Core Decodable 67

 SRA

Columbus, OH

"A live mule is stubborn."
"A robot mule is also stubborn."

What is the problem?
Doctor Hugo will tell us.

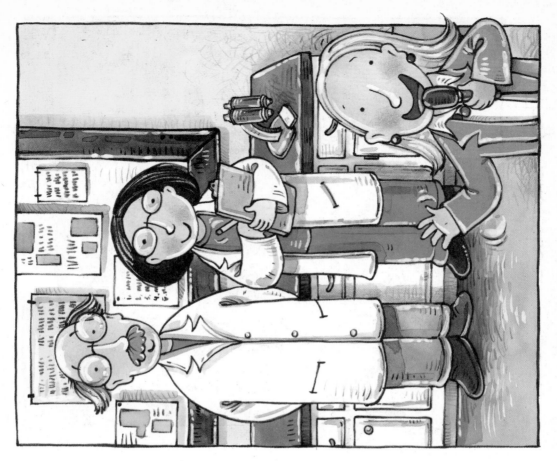

This is Doctor Hugo.
And this is Rose, a pupil.

Doctor Hugo and Rose check it.
The robot unit is not broken.

They make robots.
They made a robot mule.
What for?

A fuse is not the problem.
Is this robot unit broken?

A live mule is cute.
Will it do what humans tell it?

Fuel is not the problem.
Is it a fuse?
Rose opens the unit.

"Go!"
Nope! A live mule will not go!
It is stubborn.

Doctor Hugo is checking the fuel.
Is fuel the problem?

This is Doctor Hugo's mule.
It is not cute.

"Go! Go!"
There is a problem.
The mule will not go.

Is this robot mule stubborn?
Will it do what humans tell it?

We will have a test.
Rose will talk to the robot mule.

SRA Decodables

A Zebra

by Ethan Cruz
illustrated by Rusty Fletcher

Core Decodable 68

 SRA

Columbus, OH

For the time being, we cannot tell.
Can you spot a zebra?

8

So has the zebra left?
Or is he just well hidden?

We made a recent visit to a ranch.
We visited these horses.

We looked and looked all over.
But we did not even get a hint.

These horses have a big secret.
A zebra runs with them.

But which is the zebra?
These horses will not tell.

Summer Heat

by Frederick Prugh
illustrated by Kristen Goeters

Core Decodable 69

  SRA

Columbus, OH

25

"Mom, the beach is neat," Jean calls.
"I agree," adds Dean.

8

Jean sticks her two feet in the sea.
Dean feels the sea breeze.

It will be a hot two weeks.
Jean and Dean feel the heat.

Jean and Dean reach the beach.
The two kids see and smell the sea.

"Time for the beach you two?" asks Mom.
"Yes!" yell Jean and Dean.

4

Cars fill the streets.
They drive east to the beach.

5

Green River

by Joaquin Garcia
illustrated by Lyle Miller

Core Decodable 70

Columbus, OH

The trip is over.
But it was so exciting!

The McGraw-Hill Companies

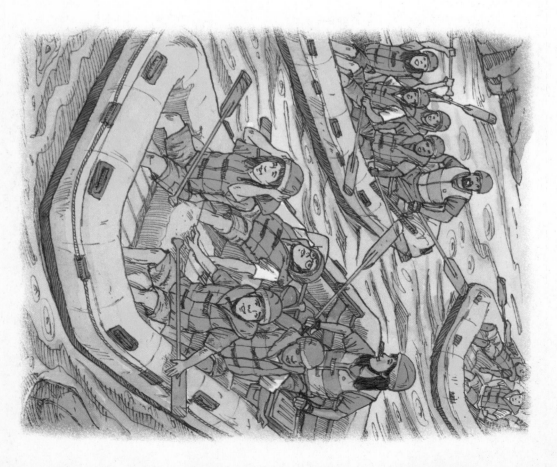

At last, the river is not so fast.
Each kid takes a deep breath.

30

These kids will take a trip.
It will be down Green River.

Rocks seem to pop up!
The rafts speed past them.

Lee leads rafting trips.
She has a team.
Her team keeps kids safe.

The rafts go faster.
Green River has little, white bubbles.

33

Each kid needs a life jacket.
Kids even need helmets.

The rafts leap up and down.
Kids smile. Kids scream.

The kids and team have three rafts.
The kids sit on raft seats.

The kids paddle hard and deep.
The river splashes faces.

At first, the trip is not fast.
Kids see fish in the clean river.

Then the river is between steep cliffs.
The rafts go faster.

Kids paddle past big rocks and green trees.
The sun shines on Green River.

8

Lee looks up.
She spots an eagle.
The kids see it.

9

SRA Decodables

A Party for Puppies

by Anne O'Brien
illustrated by Olivia Cole

Core Decodable 71

SRA

Columbus, OH

The party is over.
Happy puppies help clean up.
"Thanks for the help," Billy mutters.

The McGraw-Hill Companies

Nellie gets more yummy treats.
"No more help, please!" yells Nellie.

38

39

Nellie has garden treats.
Billy places a treat on every plate.
Every puppy helps.

Nellie and Billy have fun parties.
They invite Nellie's babies and teddies.

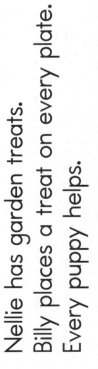

Nellie gets a table. Billy sets the table.
Every puppy helps.

4

Nellie makes funny party hats.
Billy tapes ribbons on every hat.

5

SRA Decodables

A Fancy Jacket

by David Nguyen
illustrated by Susan Lexa

Core Decodable 72

Mc Graw Hill SRA

Columbus, OH

Mom made hot, spicy tea.
"I feel better," said Nancy.
"Hot, spicy tea is for winter."

8

41

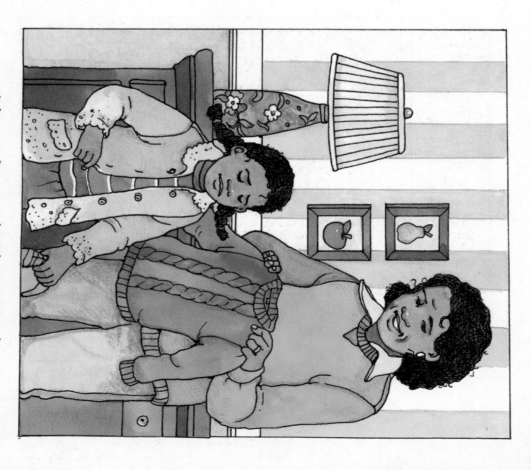

Nancy's teeth chattered.
"Yes, it is lacy," said Nancy.
"It isn't for winter."

Nancy's fancy jacket was thin.
She could feel the winter chill.

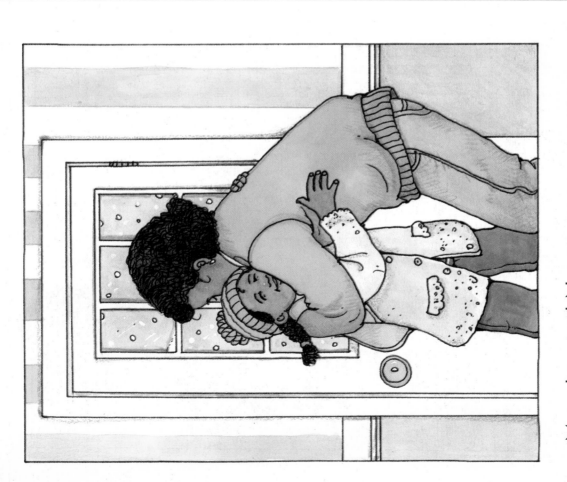

Mom hugged Nancy.
"That fancy jacket is thin," Mom said.

Nancy wished she could run.
But the sidewalk was icy.
She could fall.

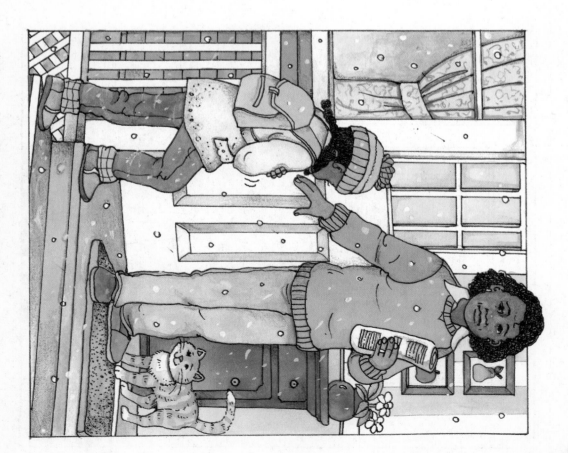

Mom looked at Nancy.
She could tell Nancy was freezing.

SRA Decodables

Skating

by Martha Wood
illustrated by Diane Paterson

Core Decodable 73

McGraw Hill **SRA**

Columbus, OH

All these kids can skate.
Have you had a chance to skate?

SRAonline.com

SRA

Copyright © 2008 by SRA/McGraw-Hill.

Printed in the United States of America.

Send all inquiries to this address:
SRA/McGraw-Hill
4400 Easton Commons
Columbus, OH 43219

This girl races on skates.
At some places, she races on ice.
At some places, she races on cement.

Some boys and girls skate on ice.
Some boys and girls skate on cement.

3

Since this boy was three, he has skated.
He skates on cement.

6

4

This girl takes lessons at City Center. She skates in fancy circles.

5

This boy also ice skates. He is fast, but not fancy.

SRA Decodables

Marcy and Sally

by Howard Lee
illustrated by Lorinda Cauley

Core Decodable 74

Mc Graw Hill **SRA**

Columbus, OH

Sally opened a fancy box.
Sally liked her gift. She hugged Marcy.

16

49

These ideas helped Marcy plan a gift.
Then, Marcy made a gift.

51

Marcy's home was next to Sally's.
Sally was Marcy's best pal.

Sally also liked the circus.
Here, Sally was at the circus and smiling.

But Sally had to go.
Her mom got a job in a big city.

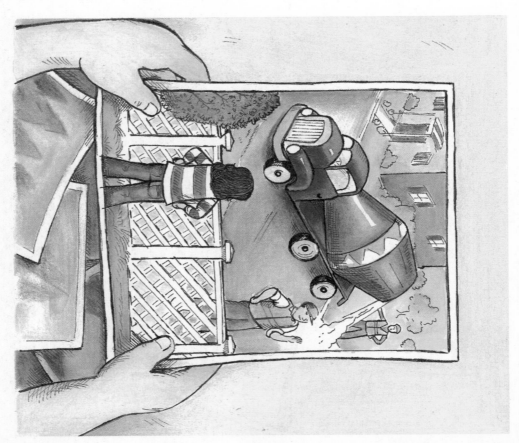

And Sally liked trucks!
She liked cement trucks.
Sally liked big vans.

There was going to be a block party.
It was for Sally and her mom and dad.

Marcy looked at Sally some more.
Sally could skate fast.
She could skate in circles.

Marcy was sad.
She was going to miss Sally.

Sally liked music.
She could sing.
Sally could dance.

Kids planned to have gifts for Sally.
Some kids shopped for gifts.
Some kids made gifts.

Marcy looked at Sally.
It helped Marcy think.

At first, Marcy did not have a gift.
She could not shop for a gift.
Marcy had just ten pennies.

What could Marcy make for Sally?
Marcy had to think.
What did Sally like?

SRA Decodables

A Gray, Rainy Day

by Dennis Fertig
illustrated by Kersti Frigell

Core Decodable 75

SRA

Columbus, OH

57

"I will play," said Jay.
"I like to play when it is rainy and gray."

8

The McGraw-Hill Companies

2

Kay went back to find Jay.
"It is gray and rainy!" said Kay.

7

58

"Will you play for us?" asked Kay.
"I will play on a gray, rainy day," said Jay.

3

Kay set up the gray painting.
The hose sprayed.

6

59

Kay liked to hear Jay play.
Kay had a way to make Jay play.

4

Kay made a gray painting.
Then Kay fixed the hose to spray.

5

60

SRA Decodables

The Opossum at Night

by Anne O'Brien

illustrated by Deborah Colvin Borgo

Core Decodable 76

McGraw Hill SRA

Columbus, OH

61

It is time for sleep.

The opossum stays with her babies.

They might play later at night.

8

The opossum returns to her tree.
Her babies wait for her.

Opossums do not like the light.
Daytime is bright.
An opossum sees better at night.

Night is over. It begins to get light.

When it is night, an opossum wakes.
She hunts for insects to feed her babies.

4

A dog frightens the opossum.
The opossum freezes. She stays still and
plays dead.

5

Why, Bly?

by Dottie Raymer
illustrated by Kersti Frigell

Core Decodable 77

SRA

Columbus, OH

"My head feels better in sand," explains Bly.

8

SRAonline.com

Mc Graw Hill

SRA

Printed in the United States of America.

Send all inquiries to this address:
SRA/McGraw-Hill
4400 Easton Commons
Columbus, OH 43219

"Is Bly too shy?" asks a child.
"I am not too shy," Bly replies.

Bly likes her head in dry sand.
Her pals don't understand why.

3

"Why not fly in the sky?" asks Eagle.
"I can't fly. I am too big," replies Bly.

6

4

"Why not lie in the sun?" asks Snake.
"I get too hot in the sun," Bly replies.

5

"Why not climb trees?" asks Chimp.
"I can't climb trees," Bly replies.

SRA Decodables

Wait for Me

by Sidney Allen
illustrated by Diane Paterson

Core Decodable 78

 SRA

Columbus, OH

69

That day, the kids raced.
Ray stayed with them.
It was a tie!

The McGraw-Hill Companies

2

Ray was riding alone.
"I am flying, Dad!" he yelled.

15

"Wait for me," called Ray.
But the kids were way ahead.

Ray pedaled fast.
Dad let the bike go.
Could Ray tell?

It was like this every day.
Ray kept trying.
But he could not keep up.

"Try riding this way," said Dad.
Dad held the bike as Ray pedaled.
Dad ran next to him.

This time, the kids stopped on the corner.
But they came right back.

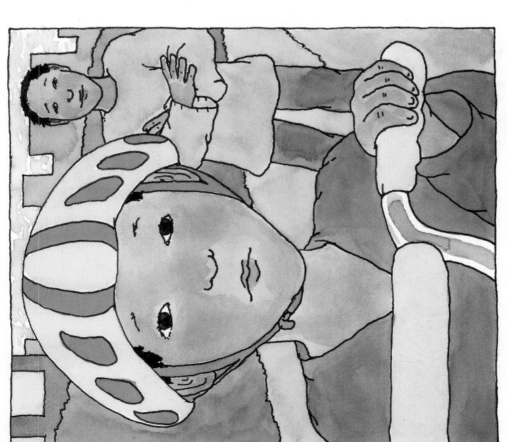

Ray was glad.
But he was a little afraid.
He might need training wheels.

The kids passed Ray.
Ray turned his bike.
"Wait for me," he called.

Ray spotted his bike in the bright sun.
It did not have training wheels!

Why was Ray always far back?
His bike still had training wheels.

The next day, Dad called Ray.
"Go to the driveway," said Dad.

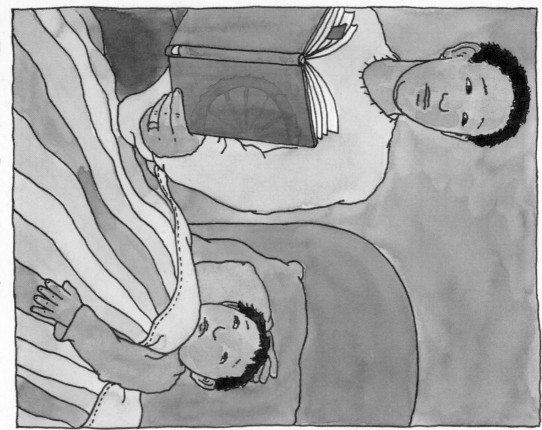

That night, Ray was sad.
"Why do you feel bad?" Dad asked.

8

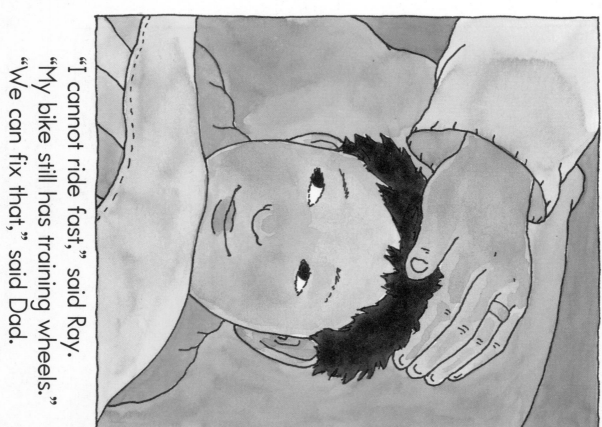

"I cannot ride fast," said Ray.
"My bike still has training wheels."
"We can fix that," said Dad.

9

SRA Decodables

Crow and Goat

by Marilee Robin Burton
illustrated by Len Epstein

Core Decodable 79

SRA

Columbus, OH

"The boat has no sail!" yelled Toad.
"I think we must row," moaned Goat.

8

SRAonline.com

SRA

"This boat only floats," mumbled Crow. Goat groaned.

But the wind did not blow, and their boat did not go.
Their boat did not go fast or slow.

6

Crow and Goat went to their boat.
Crow and Goat hoped to see their pal Toad.

3

"Let's go fast, not slow!" said Goat.
"We will go fast in this boat!" boasted Crow.

4

"Let the wind blow!" bellowed Goat.
"Here we go!" yelled Crow.

5

Decodables

Rescue that Cat!

by Linda Smith
illustrated by Kersti Frigell

Core Decodable 80

SRA

Columbus, OH

Do not argue. We all value the cat.
She will rescue the cat. The cat mews.

8

SRAonline.com

Mc Graw Hill **SRA**

Yes, let's not argue.
Few value the cat like you.
You can rescue the cat.

A cat mews in a tree.
Will you rescue that cat?

Let's not argue. We all value the cat.
You can rescue the cat.

The cat continues to mew.
I will rescue the cat.

You will rescue the cat?
No, I will rescue the cat.
Few like the cat as much as I do.

"Boat or not," I said.
"You must wait in line."
And they did.

16

SRA Decodables

Eat at Joan's

by Frederick Prugh
illustrated by Jane McCreary

Core Decodable 81

McGraw Hill SRA

Columbus, OH

85

But then I got it.
Fuel meant stuff to eat.
The men were hungry!

My name is Joan.
I own this shop.
The shop is on the coast.

I was confused.
Sailboats do not need fuel.
Wind makes sailboats go.

My shop is a drive-in.
Cars drive in and out.
Drivers get a meal at a value price.

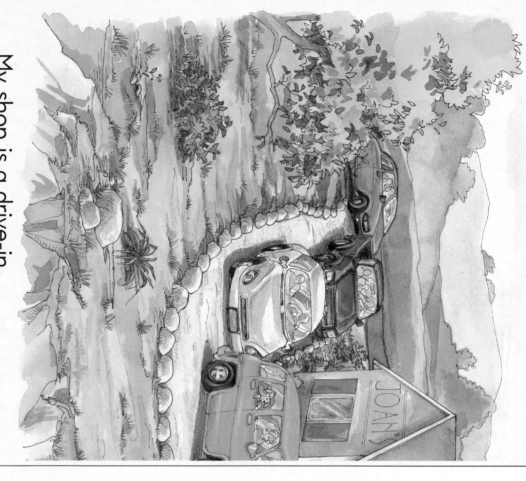

The men talked to me.
"We need fuel," they said.

I make a few yummy dishes.
I make my own veggie roast.
I make my own meatloaf.

5

A rowboat left the boat.
Men rowed it to the coast.

12

The sun went down slowly.
I looked at the sea.
A lone boat sailed on the waves.

6

Still I could see the boat.
It was sailing to the coast.
Then it stopped.

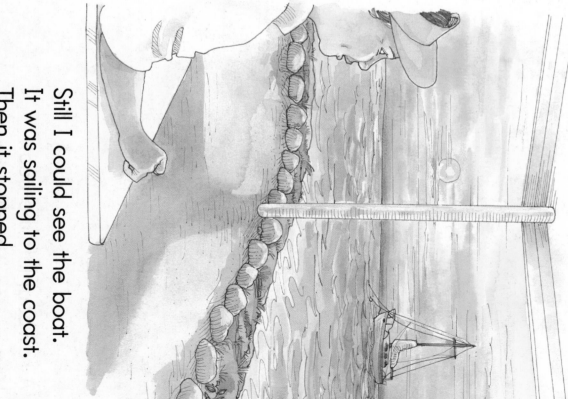

11

91

A gentle wind was blowing.
The sailboat was not far away.

I had to stay at the window.
I had to hand out dinners.
I had to do it fast.

Lots of boats have passed this way.
But few have stopped.
Why did this boat sail closer?

But I could not look.
Lots of cars were in line.
They filled the road.

SRA Decodables

A Cool Balloon

by Alex Yu
illustrated by Alex Wallner

Core Decodable 82

SRA

Columbus, OH

A first grader looked at the balloon.
It looked like a floating apple.
"Cool," she said.

8

The *McGraw-Hill* Companies

2

The riders spotted a goose flying below.
They could see a jet zoom high over them.

At first, the balloon just drooped.
But it pumped up fast.
Soon it was filled and ready.

3

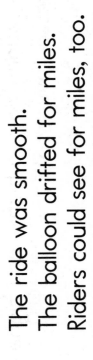

The ride was smooth.
The balloon drifted for miles.
Riders could see for miles, too.

6

Riders climbed in the basket.
A man set the balloon loose.

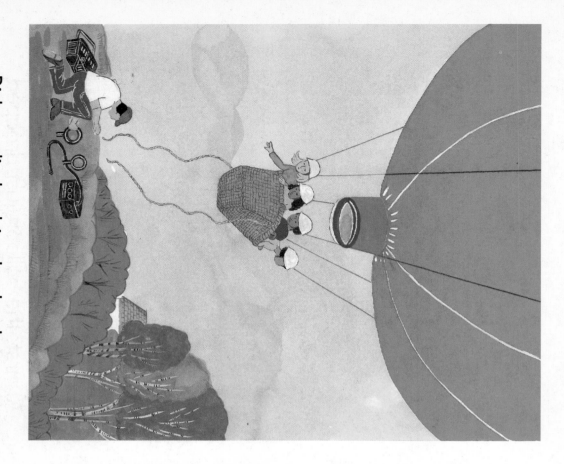

The balloon floated higher and higher.
It passed over roofs.
"Cool!" said a rider.

SRA Decodables

A True Bird

by Maria Johnson
illustrated by Lorinda Cauley

Core Decodable 83

Mc Graw Hill **SRA**

Columbus, OH

"I see the truth!" yelled Sue.
"It's hard to fool you, Sue," Ruth said.

8

The McGraw-Hill Companies

Ruth had glued a paper bird on the stick.
It was not a true bird.

Sue spotted a bird.
What kind was it?
She did not have one clue.

3

Sue spotted Ruth in the yard.
Ruth had a stick.

6

99

The bird had one blue wing.
It had one ruby red wing.
Birds don't have wings like that!

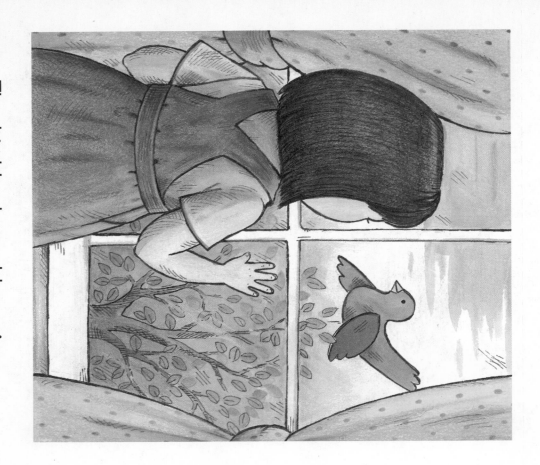

And birds fly.
This one just jumped a bit.
"Is this a true bird?" asked Sue.

Ants: The True Story

by Robert Bridges
illustrated by John Hovell

Core Decodable 84

SRA

Columbus, OH

So this is the real story.
It is all true.
Ants fool humans.

16

The McGraw-Hill Companies

I can float on my back.
I can see the moon.

Ants fool humans.
Humans think we just dig nests.
They think we dig like bugs.

3

103

Ants get exercise, too.
We swim in a pool under a glass roof.
Some ants dance in tutus.

14

But that is not the truth.
We use tools to dig.
We use drills and spades.

Some ants read.
Some read papers.
I am reading a story.

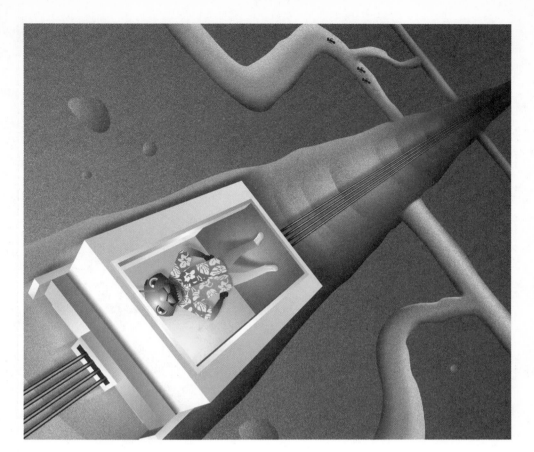

And ants do not walk down.
We zoom down in nests.
It is a fast, smooth ride.

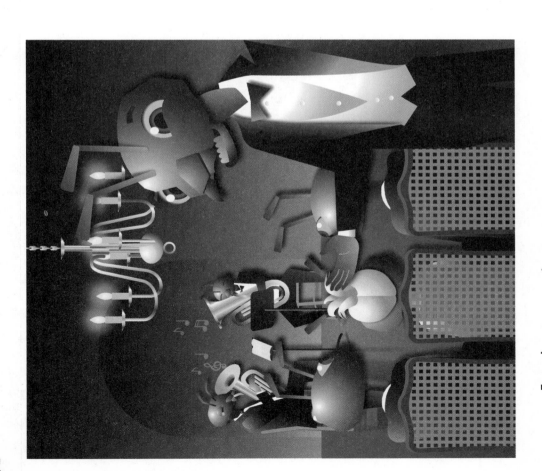

In the evening, ants rest.
Some hear music.
Two ants play a tuba duet.

Down below we have rooms.
The rooms have walls.
My room is painted blue.

After we eat, we clean up.
Ants must do their duty.
I use a broom.

107

Humans think we store food.
Well, we truly do.
But not the way humans think.

7

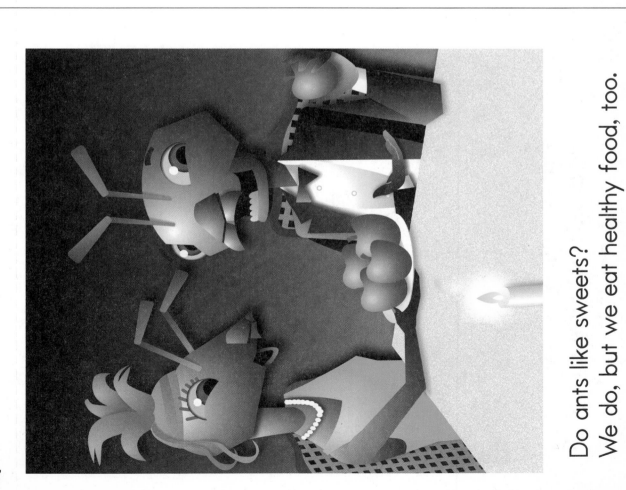

Do ants like sweets?
We do, but we eat healthy food, too.

10

This room is for food.
We keep this room cool.
Then food stays fresh.

What do ants eat?
Humans do not have a clue!
Ants eat the best food.

Drew had his flute.
Drew played the new tune.
He played the tune very well!

8

SRA Decodables

A New Tune

by Charles Broderick
illustrated by Lyle Miller

Core Decodable 85

SRA

Columbus, OH

SRA
Mc
Graw
Hill

SRAonline.com

Copyright © 2008 by SRA/McGraw-Hill.

Printed in the United States of America.

Send all inquiries to this address:
SRA/McGraw-Hill
4400 Easton Commons
Columbus, OH 43219

2

It was a very hot summer day.
Flags flew high.
It was time for Drew to play.

7

Drew played his flute.
He played in his room every day.

Drew's fingers hurt!
But he still played his flute.
He played every day in June.

Drew played a new tune.
The new tune was very hard.
He did not play it very well.

Drew played and played the tune.
He blew and blew.
Drew had to get it right.

SRA Decodables

A Good Ride

by Andrea Patel
illustrated by Tom Leonard

Core Decodable 86

SRA

Columbus, OH

113

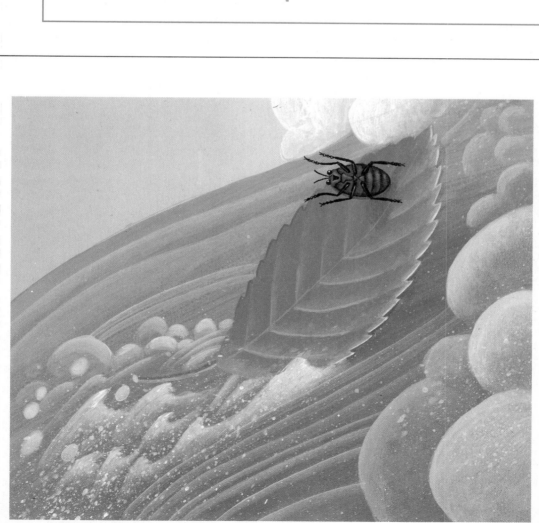

The bug rode down the falls!
"I took a good ride!" she said.

8

SRAonline.com

Mc Graw Hill

SRA

Copyright © 2008 by SRA/McGraw-Hill.

All rights reserved. The contents, or parts thereof, may be reproduced in print form for non-profit educational use with *Imagine It!* provided such reproductions bear copyright notice, but may not be reproduced in any form for any other purpose without the prior written consent of The McGraw-Hill Companies, Inc., including, but not limited to, network storage or transmission, or broadcast for distance learning. An Open Court Curriculum.

Printed in the United States of America.

Send all inquiries to this address:
SRA/McGraw-Hill
4400 Easton Commons
Columbus, OH 43219

Look at the high falls!
"I am afraid," the bug called.
Now she shook and shook.

A bug jumped on a leaf in a brook.
"Now I will take a ride," she said.

3

The stream took a sharp turn.
Now it was a fast river.
The leaf shook.

6

The bug had a foot in the brook.
She looked ahead.

The brook was now a quick stream.
"This is a good ride," said the bug.
She stood up.

SRA Decodables

Mom's Book

by Cecilia Winters
illustrated by Susan Lexa

Core Decodable 87

McGraw Hill SRA

Columbus, OH

"A camping trip?" asked Luke.
"Yes," said Mom. "You can make a book, too."

16

The McGraw-Hill Companies

The book had blank pages.

"You can fill those on a trip this June," said Mom.

118

Mom looked at a book.
"Is that book good?" asked Luke.
Mom smiled.

119

Just then Dad walked in. He had a new book.
"This is for you, Luke," said Dad.

"I like it," said Mom. "The truth is I made it."
"You did?" asked Luke.

4

"Yes," said Mom. "There is the proof."
A snapshot was glued to a page.

13

121

"The trip was fun," said Mom. "I even spotted a moose."

"A moose!" said Luke.

12

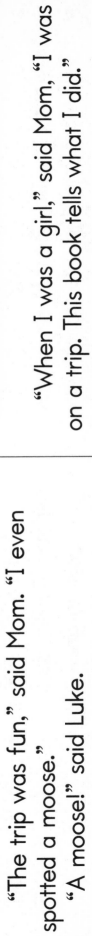

"When I was a girl," said Mom, "I was on a trip. This book tells what I did."

5

"I went camping," said Mom. "I was with my mom and dad. We took a van."

"I threw in too much salt. Three big spoons," Mom said.
Her grin grew bigger.

Mom showed Luke a page.
"I drew a map," said Mom. "It shows
the way."

7

"Did you cook food?" asked Luke.
"Yes," Mom grinned. "I made bad stew!"

10

"The trip was in June," said Mom. "I said that it was hot. But it was cool at night."

8

"We had a new tent," said Mom. "It was dark blue. I drew that, too."

9

SRA Decodables

A Clown in Town

by Dina McClellan
illustrated by Len Epstein

Core Decodable 88

 SRA

Columbus, OH

The Browns took the bus out of town. On the way home, Howie said, "Wow! Clowns are much better than rain showers."

8

Chowder the Clown did tricks. He made a cat bark and a dog meow.

Rain showers are good for flowers, but not for the Brown family. The Browns were tired of being inside.

3

It was hot and crowded, but the Browns did not care.

6

"How can we see clowns?" asked Howie.
"Is the circus in town?" asked Dad.

4

"Yes! There are clowns at the circus in town," said Mom.
The Browns ran down the stairs and rode the bus to town.

5

Max the Grouch

by Joyce Mallery
illustrated by Len Epstein

Core Decodable 89

 SRA

Columbus, OH

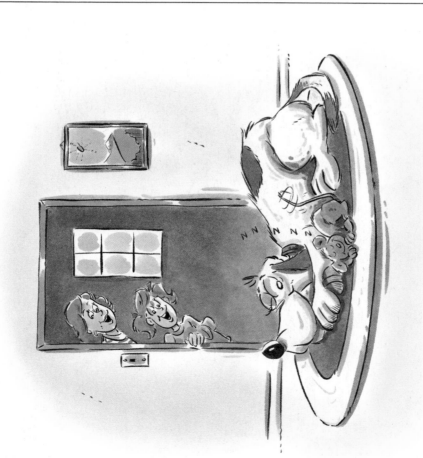

Pat went to feed Max.
"Look, Mom!" Pat whispered.
"Max found a mouse pal!"
Max was finally happy.

8

SRA
Mc
Graw
Hill

SRAonline.com

Copyright © 2008 by SRA/McGraw-Hill.

All rights reserved. The contents, or parts thereof, may be reproduced in print form for non-profit educational use with *Imagine It!* provided such reproductions bear copyright notice, but may not be reproduced in any form for any other purpose without the prior written consent of The McGraw-Hill Companies, Inc., including, but not limited to, network storage or transmission, or broadcast for distance learning. An Open Court Curriculum.

Printed in the United States of America.

Send all inquiries to this address:
SRA/McGraw-Hill
4400 Easton Commons
Columbus, OH 43219

"How about a long walk?" asked Pat.
She and Max walked around the park.
Now Max was a tired grouch.

Pat hugged her hound, Max.
But Max was a grouch!
What will make Max happy?

3

Max spit the bone out of his mouth.
He made a loud sound!
Max was still a grouch.

6

"Maybe Max needs a new doghouse," said Mom.
But Max was still a grouch.

4

"How about a pound of dog bones?" asked Dad.
Dad set a large bone on the ground.

5

133

SRA Decodables

King Knox and His Knight

by Joyce Mallery
illustrated by Len Epstein

Core Decodable 90

SRA

Columbus, OH

The knight packed a knapsack and went away.
The knight was now happy.

8

SRAonline.com

SRA

Copyright © 2008 by SRA/McGraw-Hill.

All rights reserved. The contents, or parts thereof, may be reproduced in print form for non-profit educational use with *Imagine It!* provided such reproductions bear copyright notice, but may not be reproduced in any form for any other purpose without the prior written consent of The McGraw-Hill Companies, Inc., including, but not limited to, network storage or transmission, or broadcast for distance learning. An Open Court Curriculum.

Printed in the United States of America.

Send all inquiries to this address:
SRA/McGraw-Hill
4400 Easton Commons
Columbus, OH 43219

The McGraw-Hill Companies

The knight got down on his knee.
"I know I don't want to be a knight," he replied.

King Knox told his knight to do things.
"I want you to tie knots," ordered King Knox.
"I don't know how," replied his knight.

3

King Knox was getting mad.
"You don't know how to do much. What do you know?"

6

"I want you to sharpen this knife," ordered King Knox.
"I don't know how," replied his knight.

4

"I want you to knit socks," ordered King Knox.
"I don't know how," replied his knight.

5

SRA Decodables

Foul Ball!

by Joaquin Garcia
illustrated by Lyle Miller

Core Decodable 91

SRA
Mc Graw Hill

Columbus, OH

Gramps frowned a bit. Then he smiled and gave it back. "No thanks, Jay," said Gramps.
Gramps felt even prouder of Jay.

16

Jay held the round ball for a second. Then he gave it to Gramps. "This ball is for you, Gramps," said Jay.

Jay looked down at the baseball field. It was so green. "Wow!" said Jay to Gramps.

3

"How about that catch!" shouted Gramps. Jay looked at the ball. Jay looked at Gramps.

14

Lots of fans sat around Jay. The crowd was huge. The fans all came to see the Owls.

The foul ball bounced by Jay's knee. Now was his chance. Jay knelt and got the foul ball! Gramps felt proud.

141

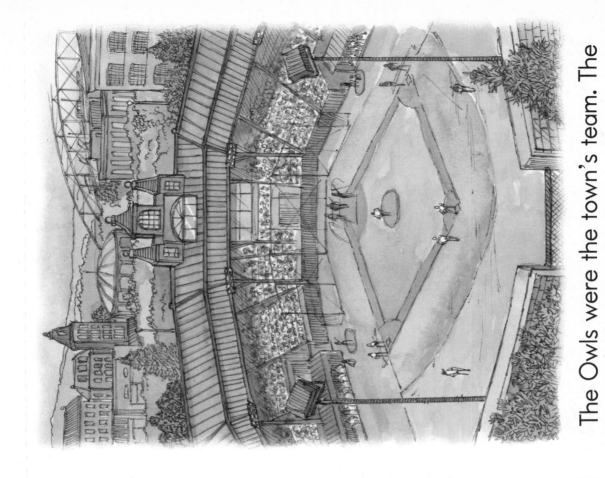

The Owls were the town's team. The Owls played at Brown Park.

But the ball did not reach them. Instead, it hit a cement step. It made a loud sound as it bounced.

Jay was thrilled. It was hard to get Owls tickets. But Gramps had found a way.

6

It was a high foul ball. The ball flew in the stands close to Jay and Gramps!

11

143

"I like these seats," said Jay. "We could catch a foul ball."

"Maybe," said Gramps.

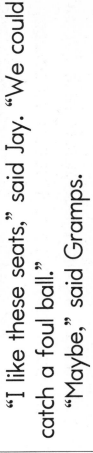

The best hitter was up. The pitch was fast. Pow! He knocked the ball way up!

Gramps had seen lots of Owls games. But Gramps never got a foul ball. Jay knew that.

8

Soon the game started. The crowd was loud. Fans shouted, "Go, Owls, go!"

9

144

SRA Decodables

Paul's Sauce

by Howard Lee
illustrated by Liz Callen

Core Decodable 92

McGraw Hill SRA

Columbus, OH

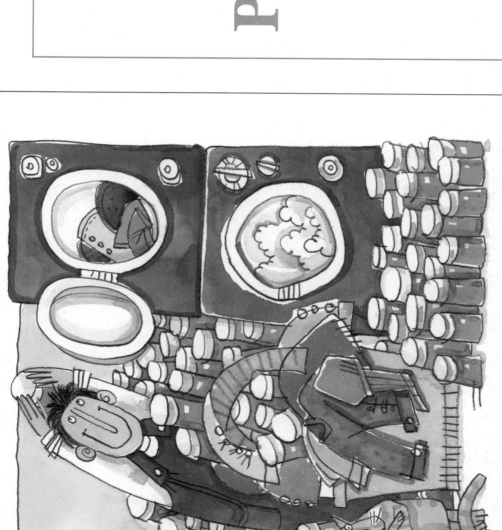

Paul makes jars and jars of sauce. I saw them in his basement and in his laundry. Paul, stop making sauce!

8

Paul mixes his sauce with straw for the cows.

Paul's cat gets saucers of sauce. The cat has sauce on its paws!

7

Paul likes to cook. He makes sauce.
Because he likes it, he makes a lot.

3

But Paul mixes sauce with cereal and
raw beets. That tastes awful!

6

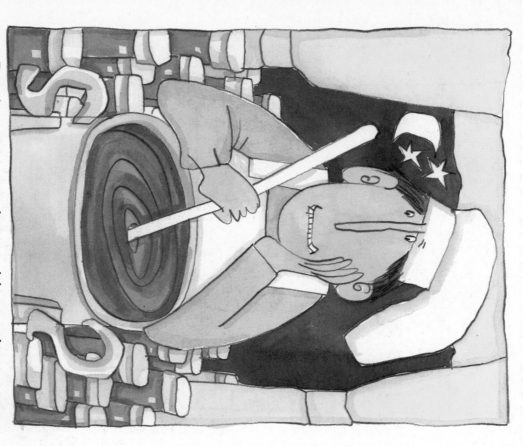

Paul starts at dawn. He makes sauce all day. He yawns at night. But he still makes sauce.

4

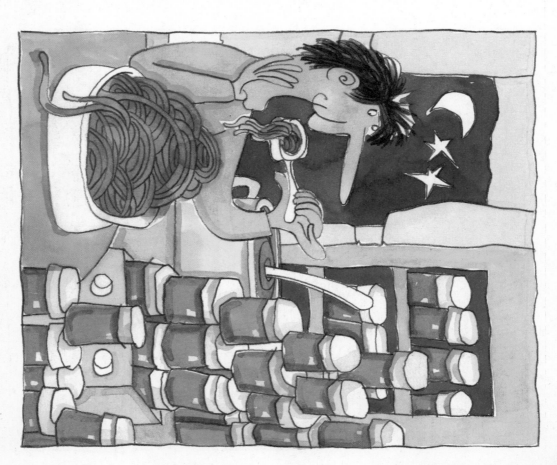

Paul uses sauce a lot. He mixes it with noodles and meat. That is fine.

5

Mr. Daw Thought

by Frederick Prugh
illustrated by Nicole Rutten

Core Decodable 93

SRA

Columbus, OH

The concert ended with applause. "I am clapping for the music," he thought. "And because I stayed awake!"

8

The McGraw-Hill Companies

2

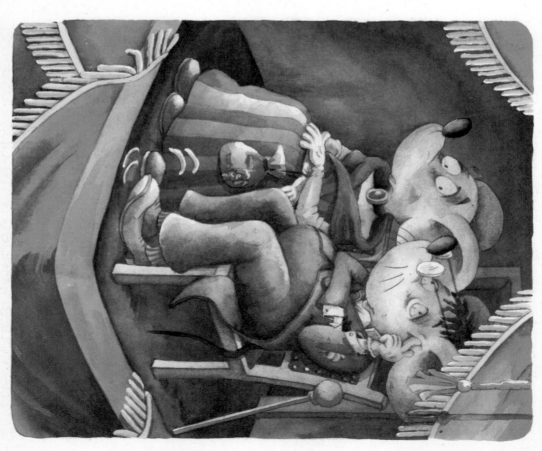

Mr. Daw started to tap his foot. "Tapping ought to keep me awake," he thought.

7

150

Mr. Daw was so tired. He brought heavy loads of cheese into his shop all day.

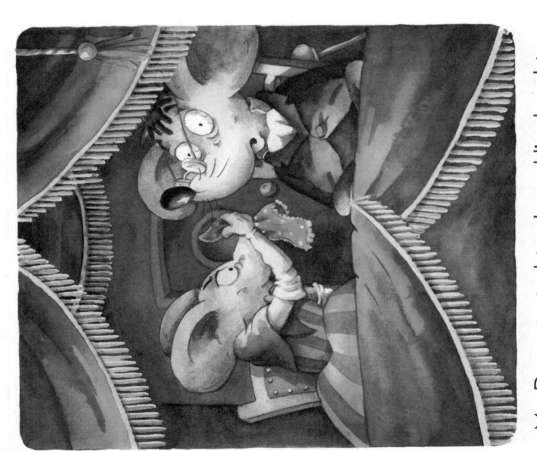

Mr. Daw started to doze. His daughter sneezed into a cloth. He awoke. "Don't get caught sleeping!" he thought.

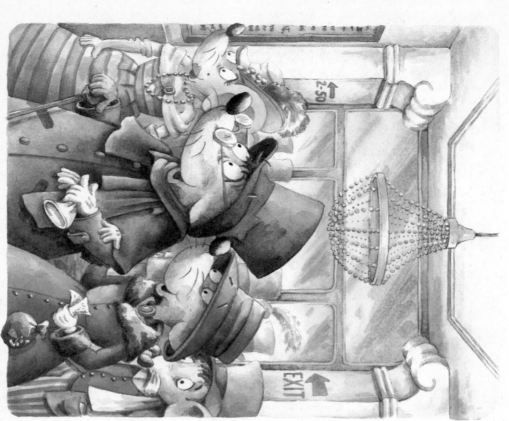

Mr. Daw could not rest. He was going into a concert hall. His daughter had bought tickets.

4

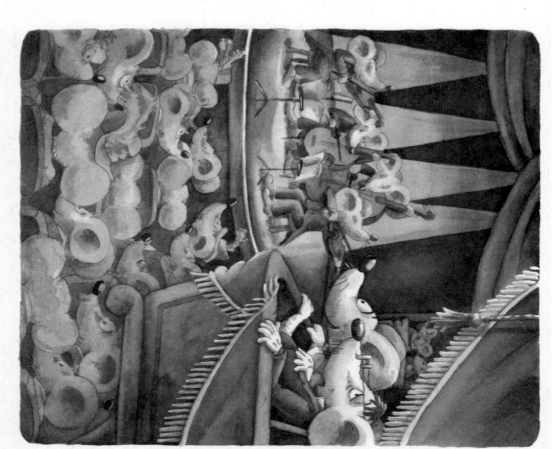

Mr. Daw liked music, but he was tired. He fought to stay awake as he sat in his seat.

5

At Dawn

by Natalie Lambert
illustrated by Kristin Goeters

Core Decodable 94

 SRA

Columbus, OH

153

Then I saw a third bunting on my awning. I was ready for fall.

16

I was happy as I drove home. But at home, I saw a second bunting on my lawn!

155

I bought a book about birds. I looked for birds shown in my book.

I could not find one bird. It was the bunting.

3

There sat a bright blue bunting! I was in shock. I saw it at last!

14

Dawn is a good time to spot birds. My dad taught me that dawn is when birds wake up.

4

I paused and looked at the hood of my auto.

13

I visited the woods every day before dawn. I brought my bird book. I looked for a bunting.

5

Soon it was time to go. I felt sad because I had not spotted a bunting.

12

I hid in the woods. I crawled in tall grass. I fought awful bugs! But I didn't spot a bunting.

6

I saw a yellow finch and a blackbird. But I did not see a bunting.

11

In the fall, the buntings had to fly away.
I had to spot a bunting before then!

7

Small birds squawked and cawed. They
saw the hawk. They did not wish to be
caught.

10

It was the last day of August. I hid in deep grass. I thought birds could not see me.

I spotted a hawk.

8

The hawk flew in a low circle. Was it because of me? No, it was looking for food.

9

SRA Decodables

Roy and Royal

by Tom Sato
illustrated by Angela Adams

Core Decodable 95

Mc Graw Hill **SRA**

Columbus, OH

Roy picked his beans. Royal dug up his bone.

That night, the boy enjoyed a good dinner. Royal enjoyed his bone.

8

The green beans grew. Rabbits tried to destroy them. But Royal spoiled the rabbits' snack. He chased them away.

Roy dug in the soil. His dog, Royal, joined him.

Roy enjoyed gardening. Royal enjoyed digging.

Roy felt joy. Green points stuck out of the soil. His green beans were growing.

Roy dropped seeds in the soil. He planted green beans. Royal planted a bone.

4

Roy used a hose. He kept the soil moist. Roy waited for the seeds to grow.

5

SRA Decodables

Little Wren's Surprise

by Joyce Mallery
illustrated by Deborah Colvin Borgo

Core Decodable 96

McGraw Hill SRA

Columbus, OH

"We were wrong," said Little Wren.

"It is a tool to fix things!"

8

A girl came into the yard.
"Here's that missing wrench!" she yelled.
"Now we can fix my bike."

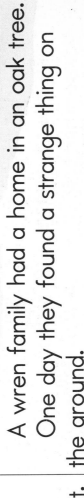

A wren family had a home in an oak tree.
One day they found a strange thing on the ground.

3

"Let's wrap it up," said Little Wren.
But the paper had a big wrinkle. It did not fit.

6

167

"What is it?" asked Dad.
He tried wriggling under it, but it
was too big.

4

"Can you write with it?" asked Mom.
Mom rubbed the side, but it didn't make
a mark.

5

SRA Decodables

The Phantom Frog

by Irene Belnik
illustrated by Kersti Frigell

Core Decodable 97

McGraw Hill SRA

Columbus, OH

"Peep, peep, peep," calls the frog. Ralph shouts, "I found the phantom. It's a little green tree frog!"

8

The McGraw-Hill Companies

Ralph looks closely at a leaf. He tells Phillip, "I can take a photo of this frog."

170

In the spring, Phillip and Ralph take a hike in the woods.

3

The boys hear "Peep, peep, peep."
"I think it's a phantom," whispers Phillip.
"Don't be silly," scolds Ralph. "Phantoms are phony."

6

Phillip finds leaves like elephant ears.
Ralph takes photographs of birds in the trees.

Then Phillip and Ralph hear "Peep, peep, peep."
Ralph whispers, "It is not a bird."
Phillip asks Ralph, "What can it be?"

It was just an old candy wrapper. It was made of gold foil. Joyce smiled. So did Phil.

16

SRA Decodables

A Hike

by William Overturf
illustrated by Jane McCreary

Core Decodable 98

Mc Graw Hill **SRA**

Columbus, OH

Phil ran to the shiny thing. It did look like gold! Phil took a close look.

The rain stopped. The hikers looked at the trail. Was it all mud? Did the rain spoil it?

3

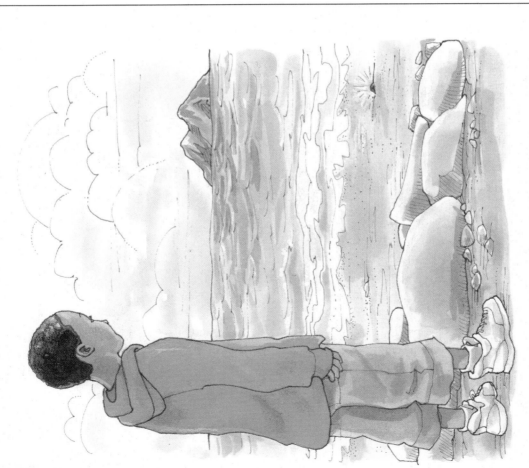

Phil looked at the sandy soil. He saw a shiny, bright thing. Was it a gold coin?

14

"The trail looks fine," said Joyce. She was the leader. Joyce looked at her wrist. "And we have time."

Joyce pointed to the beach. "Waves still bring gold coins to the beach."

Joyce smiled at the hikers.
"We can hike, boys and girls," she said
in a happy voice.

5

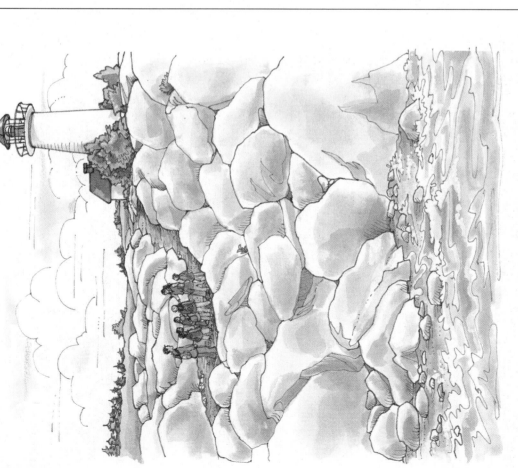

"A sailor wrote about the wreck," said
Joyce. "Lots of gold coins were sunk."

12

177

Joyce used her cell phone to call camp. "I have made a choice. We will keep hiking," she said.

6

Joyce said more. "A ship filled with gold coins hit the rocks. It was destroyed. The sailors were safe."

11

178

The sun was shining now. And there was a rainbow! Kids took photos of it. They enjoyed the hike.

"Those rocks could wreck a ship!" said Phil.

"They have," said Joyce.

The kids saw a lighthouse. By the lighthouse, waves hit big, big rocks. The waves made a loud noise.

8

At night, the lighthouse helped ships. It helped ships avoid the big rocks.

9

SRA Decodables

Earnest's Search

by Judy Mills
illustrated by Len Ebert

Core Decodable 99

SRA

Columbus, OH

181

It is a pearl! Earnest did not find gold.
Earnest found a pearl!

8

He saw a seashell stuck in the earth.
What is that inside?

Earnest liked to swim. He learned to swim under the water. He liked to search for things in the earth.

3

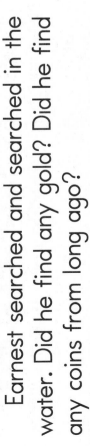

Earnest searched and searched in the water. Did he find any gold? Did he find any coins from long ago?

6

183

Earnest searched deep in the water. He heard there might be gold. Earnest searched, but he did not find any gold.

4

He swam in the water along the earth. Earnest yearned to find any item of value.

5

184

Dudley the Donkey

by Rich Lewis
illustrated by Len Epstein

Core Decodable 100

 SRA

Columbus, OH

"Dudley! Dudley! Are you going to help me haul this cart of turkeys or not?"

8

The crowd will shout, "Dudley! Dudley!"
The crowd will throw me roses and carrots!

7

If I am the winner, I will get fame and lots of cash. Maybe I will even get a key to the city.

6

I am Dudley the donkey. I am a jockey. I have a red and white shirt.

3

I will race Tracey the turkey. She is a jockey, too. She has a green and white shirt.

4

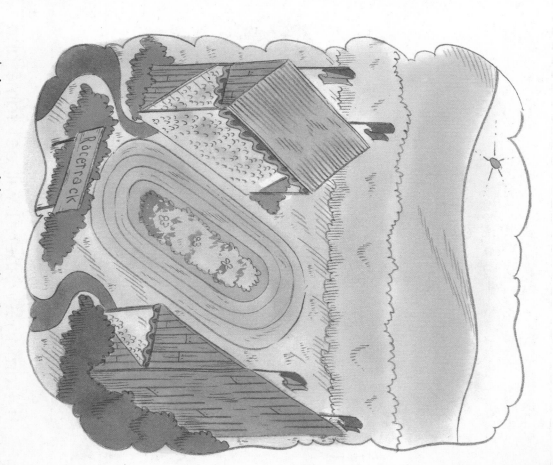

A big crowd has made the trip to the valley to see the race.

5

SRA Decodables

Casey and Earl

by Bud Hamilton
illustrated by Arvis Stewart

Core Decodable 101

McGraw Hill **SRA**

Columbus, OH

Casey gave Earl the key. Then he started to run. "Come on, pokey," yelled Casey. "We have to get home."

16

Casey showed Earl the key.
Earl smiled. "It was a good thing this time," said Earl.

"Come on, pokey!" called Earl.
Casey heard Earl.
"You walk too slowly," Earl called.

3

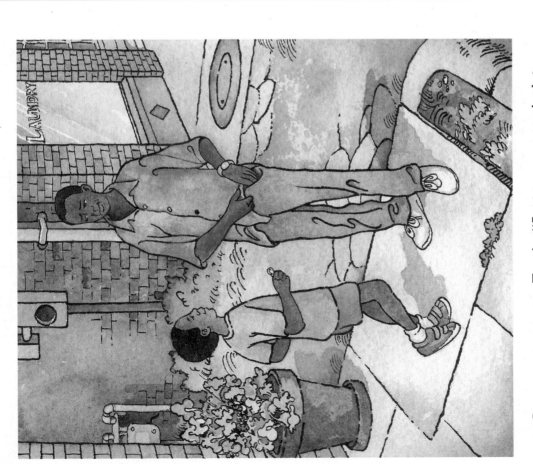

Casey ran to Earl. "It is a good thing
I am pokey," he said.
"Why?" asked Earl.

14

191

Casey did walk slowly. He liked to stop and look. He liked to learn things as he walked.

4

Casey looked at Earl. He knew what Earl was searching for. Earl must have just dropped the key.

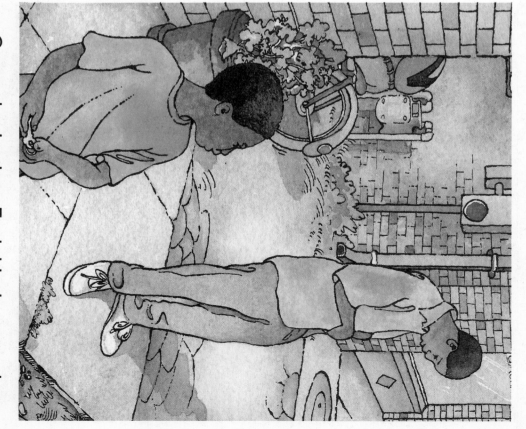

13

193

When Casey walked, he thought a lot, too. Now he was looking at a sports store. He was thinking about what he saw.

5

It was a key. Casey picked it up. It was Earl's key to the house!

12

Casey saw hockey sticks. He also saw volleyballs. Was there a game that could use both?

6

Casey still looked around. Next to the sidewalk, there was a patch of earth. He saw a gold thing there.

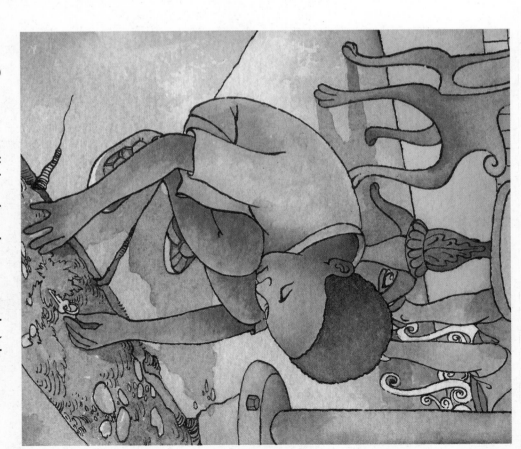

11

195

"Casey, come on. We have to get home," called Earl.

"It is still early," Casey yelled back.

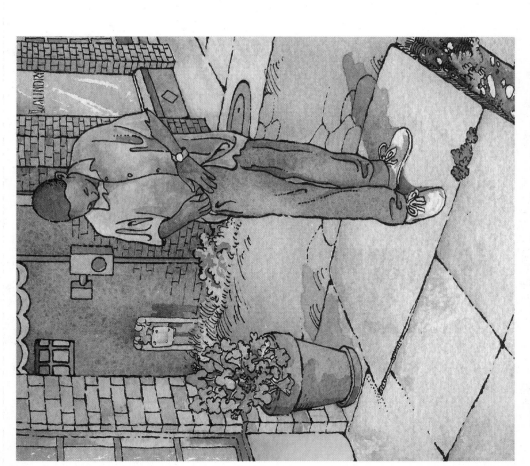

"Come on, pokey," yelled Earl. Earl was standing by the alley. He was searching his pockets.

Casey and Earl were going home. Mom was going to be late. So Earl had to start dinner soon.

8

Now Casey was thinking about the sandwich store. Did it have turkey and cheese?

9

196

SRA Decodables

Garden in the Sky

by Maria Johnson
illustrated by Len Ebert

Core Decodable 102

Mc Graw Hill **SRA**

Columbus, OH

Jackie and Max walked around the rooftop garden. Plants filled the space. "Wow! This is one big garden!" Jackie said.

16

The three walked out on the skyscraper roof. Jackie was shocked. All she could see was sky and plants.

15

198

Max and Jackie liked gardens.
"My dad's job is in a skyscraper," said Max.
"It has a big garden."

3

Max's dad set stuff on his desk.
"Time to go up," he said.
Soon the three were back on the elevator. They were going up.

14

"A garden in a skyscraper?" Jackie asked. "How can that be?"
"I will ask my dad to take us," said Max.

4

"This is a nice garden!" said Jackie.
"This is not it yet," said Max. "Just wait!"

13

One morning, Max's dad did take the kids. They rode the train. The train raced down the tracks.

5

All around were plants and flowers. Jackie thought one flower was wax. But it was real.

12

Dad, Max, and Jackie were downtown fast. They walked to a tall skyscraper. It seemed to be made of dark glass.

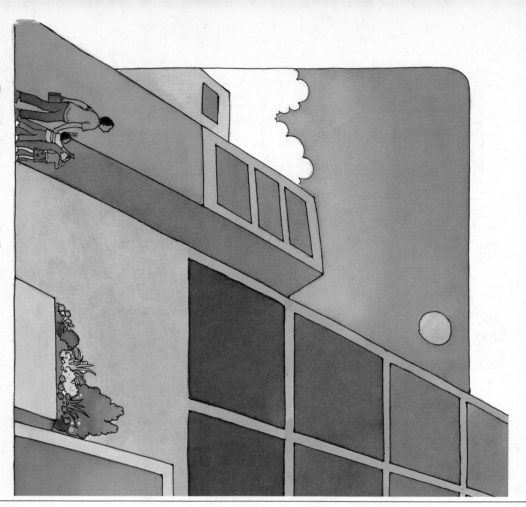

6

The elevator took them way up. It stopped, and they walked out.

"My desk is back there," said Max's dad.

11

"This is the place," said Max.
Jackie looked way up. "Wow!" she said.

7

LOBBY

"That is not the garden," said Max.
Jackie thought it looked like one.
The three stepped on the elevator.

10

On the sidewalk, there were big planters. They were filled with plants.

"Is this the garden?" asked Jackie.

"No way," said Max.

8

The three walked inside. A man with a badge said, "Good day."

By the man's desk were plants.

9

SRA Decodables

Picking Flowers

by Charles Broderick
illustrated by Dennis Hockerman

Core Decodable 103

SRA

Columbus, OH

"That's right," said Ranger Liz. "So what do you say now, Rick?"

"Please do not pick the flowers," smiled Rick.

16

SRAonline.com

SRA

Copyright © 2008 by SRA/McGraw-Hill.

Printed in the United States of America.

Send all inquiries to this address:
SRA/McGraw-Hill
4400 Easton Commons
Columbus, OH 43219

Rick was thinking. "There would be no flowers left," he said. "And that would be bad for the bees and birds."

Six kids hiked behind Ranger Liz down
the trail. The kids liked Ranger Liz.

3

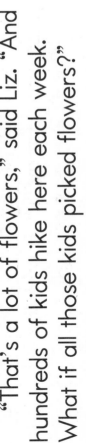

"That's a lot of flowers," said Liz. "And
hundreds of kids hike here each week.
What if all those kids picked flowers?"

14

The kids followed Ranger Liz up high ridges and over wide bridges. They followed her into a field of flowers.

4

"That's right," said Rick.

"What about your five pals?" asked Liz. "Would they like a mix, too?"

"Yes!" shouted the kids.

13

The kids really liked the flowers. Some flowers reached the trail's edge. Some looked like bright spikes.

5

"Well," said Ranger Liz. "Your mom might like a mix of flowers. You might pick six or seven."

12

"I wish I could take some flowers home," said Rick. "They would be nice for my mom."

"Read this," said Mike.

6

Rick was still thinking about his mom.

"But why can't we pick flowers?" he asked.

Ranger Liz smiled.

11

211

Rick read, "Please do not pick the flowers." Rick looked around the field. It was filled with flowers.

"See the bees and the birds," said Ranger Liz. "They need the flowers. And the flowers need them."

"There are miles of flowers," said Rick. "Why can't we pick some?" A yellow and black bee buzzed by.

8

The bee sniffed at a flower. Rick and the kids jumped back. Then Rick saw a black and yellow finch. The bird sniffed at a flower, too.

9

A Farm Visit

by William Overturf
illustrated by Meredith Johnson

Core Decodable 104

 SRA

Columbus, OH

"Donnie, you know what that means," Joan said.

"Yes," smiled Donnie. "Moo!"

"Moo!" joined in Joan.

16

2

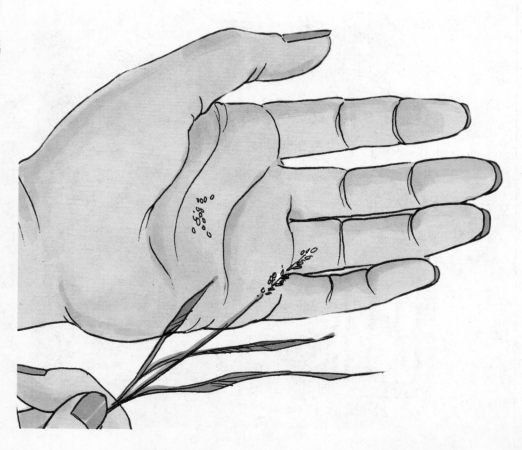

"Rice is a grass," said Miss Dock. "Seeds from it make food. And seeds from oat grass make food, too."

15

214

Miss Dock drove the bus to a farm.
The class looked out the windows. They
saw meadows, barns, and silos.

3

"Look," said Miss Dock. "This blade of
grass has little seeds on top."
Miss Dock dropped little seeds in her
hand.

14

215

Some of the meadows had wire fences. Some had low stone walls.

"Those stone walls have big rocks," said Joan.

4

Miss Dock and the kids got out of the bus. She picked a piece of very tall grass from the lawn.

13

The kids were from the city. Some had not seen a farm.

"Is that an ox?" asked Donnie.

5

Miss Dock parked the bus at the farmer's house. She looked at the farmer's lawn.

"I will show you," said Miss Dock.

12

Miss Dock smiled. "Nope, it looks a bit like an ox. But it is just a big cow."

"Ick! It is eating grass," said Joan.

6

"Rice is grass?" asked Joan.

"Oatmeal is not green," said Donnie. "How can oats be grass?"

11

219

Miss Dock slowed down the bus.
"We eat grass, too," she said.
"No way!" said Joan.
The cow was mooing now.

7

The bus was going slowly down
the road. The road had big holes. Miss
Dock had to dodge them.

10

Miss Dock drove the bus over a bumpy road.

"What did you eat for breakfast?" Miss Dock asked.

8

"A little box of Rice Puffs," Joan said.

"A bowl of oatmeal," said Donnie.

"You both had grass, then," said Miss Dock.

9

SRA Decodables

Mr. Plant Expert

by Sidney Allen
illustrated by Dominic Catalano

Core Decodable 105

SRA

Columbus, OH

Mr. Plant Expert looked at the clock.
"Thanks kids! Thanks adults! I must run
to pluck some weeds. See you next time!"

16

The McGraw-Hill Companies

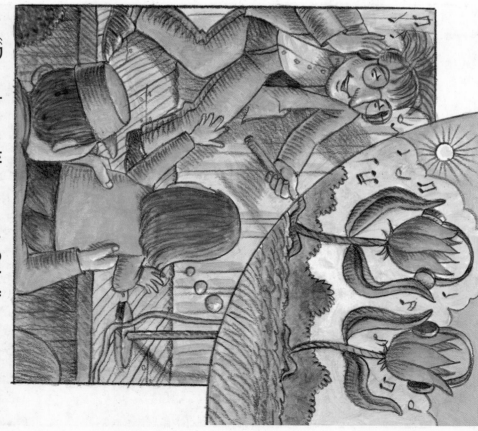

"Do plants like music? What tunes do they like?" asked a girl.

"Plant experts like music," said Mr. Expert. "I like rock tunes."

Kids and adults filled the hall. They came to see Mr. Plant Expert. They came to have fun.

"Plant can mean factory," said Mr. Expert. "A factory makes things. A brick plant makes bricks."

14

"Hi! I am Mr. Plant Expert. Ask me about plants and gardens. Maybe you can stump me!"

4

"There is a brick plant in town," said a boy. "Can bricks grow on plants?"
"No," said Mr. Expert.

13

224

"Mr. Expert," said a pupil. "I heard about a truck farm. Do huge trucks grow there? Are buses and cars grown there, too?"

5

"I am a good gardener," explained Mr. Expert. "That is what a green thumb means. But my thumbs are not really green."

12

"No," smiled Mr. Expert. "Veggies grow on truck farms. The veggies are cucumbers, beans, and so on."

6

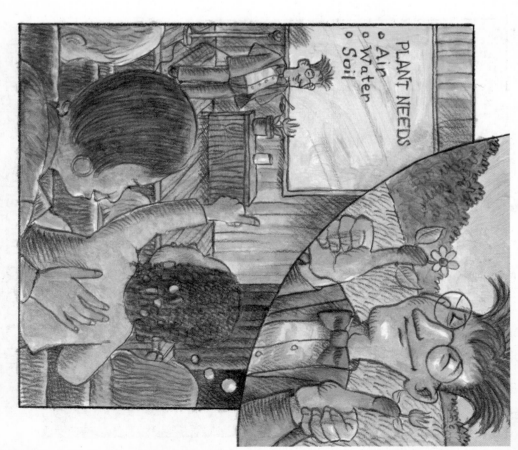

"My mom said you have a green thumb. Can I see it?" asked a cute kid. Mr. Expert chuckled.

11

"Farmers pack veggies in boxes. Trucks take the veggies to stores. That is why the farms are called truck farms."

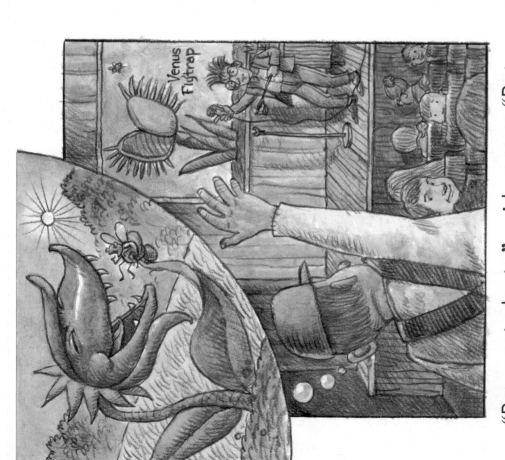

"Bugs eat plants," said a man. "But do plants eat bugs?"

"A few do," said Mr. Expert. "They are good to take to picnics."

"Is this true?" asked a boy. "Do plants get fuel from the sun? How can a hose reach that far?"

"Plants do get fuel from the sun," explained Mr. Expert. "But plants do not use hoses. Sunshine provides plants with fuel and energy."

SRA Decodables

Weeds or Flowers

by Howard Lee
illustrated by Susan Jaekel

Core Decodable 106

SRA

Columbus, OH

It is good to fight weeds and make a garden pretty. And it is good to help your mom and dad.

16

Now gardeners plant goldenrod. It is pretty. Butterflies like these bright flowers.

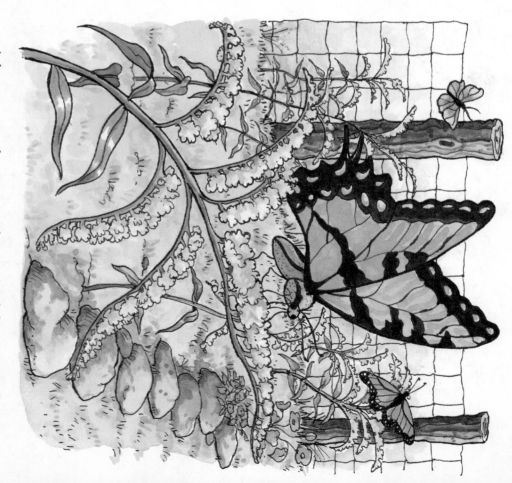

Lots of kids help in the garden.
Some pick weeds. Can you? It can be
hard on your knees and hands!

3

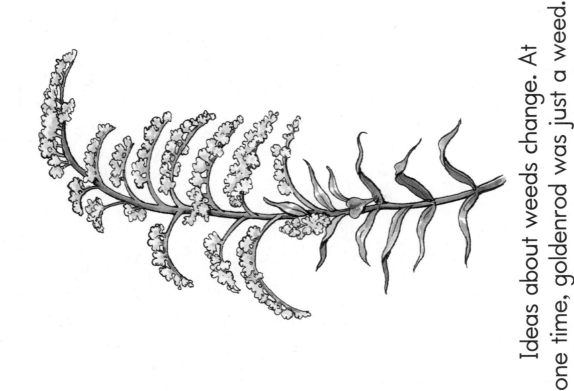

Ideas about weeds change. At
one time, goldenrod was just a weed.
Doctors thought it made humans
sneeze. It did not.

14

Can you tell a good plant from a weed? At times, it is easy. At times, it is hard. At times, even adults make mistakes.

4

Some farmers plant sunflowers. They sell sunflower seeds. And some farmers call sunflowers weeds. Why? The golden flower can wreck cornfields.

13

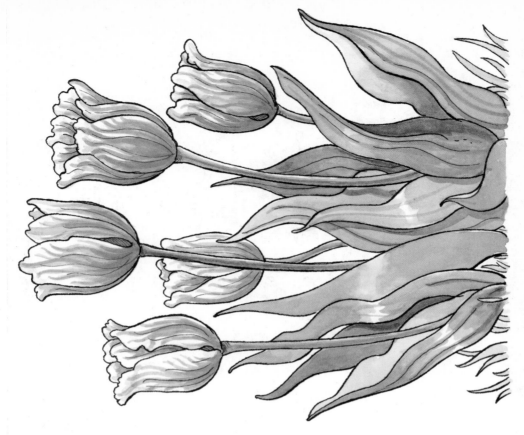

See the plant on this page. It might be in your garden. It is a tulip. It has a pretty flower. It is not a weed.

5

Gardeners and most kids like sunflowers. Bright sunflowers might make you smile. You would not call it a weed.

12

See this plant. It is pretty, too. It is purple loosestrife. It grows on sides of roads. It is a weed. Why?

6

But in your yard, clover is a weed. It stops the remaining plants from growing.

11

234

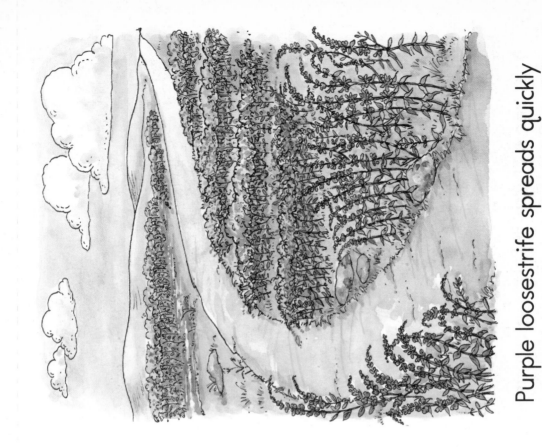

Purple loosestrife spreads quickly over a field. Soon it takes all the space. Good plants die. So purple loosestrife is a weed.

7

This plant is sweet clover. Farmers like it to feed cows. And this clover makes farmland better.

10

235

You know this plant. It is a dandelion. In spring, fields of dandelions look very pretty. But then the yellow flower changes.

8

Dandelion flowers turn to puffballs. Winds blow them away. Ugly leaves are left. The puffballs are seeds. They make even more weeds!

9

A Family House

by Ethan Cruz
illustrated by Renate Lohmann

Core Decodable 107

SRA
Mc Graw Hill

Columbus, OH

The family of four stood on the grassy hill. They looked at the new house below. "We are so lucky," Dean said.

16

The McGraw-Hill Companies

Finally, after weeks and weeks, the house was ready. A big van brought beds, dressers, desks, and tables.

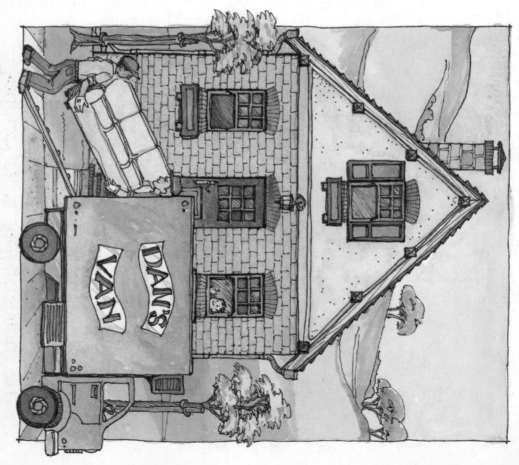

Dean, Mom, and the baby sat on a grassy hill. A tractor dug below. The tractor dug a deep hole.

3

Four trees were planted. Carpenters put a deck on the back of the house. "We will eat there at times," said Mom.

14

The tractor piled dirt on the field's edge.

"That hole will be the basement," explained Mom. "And trucks will haul that dirt away."

4

Weeks passed. Walls were plastered. Lights and switches were added. Painters came. Soon the house was almost ready.

PETE'S PLASTER

13

Dean was happy. This hole was the start of a new house. It was his family's new house! He felt lucky.

5

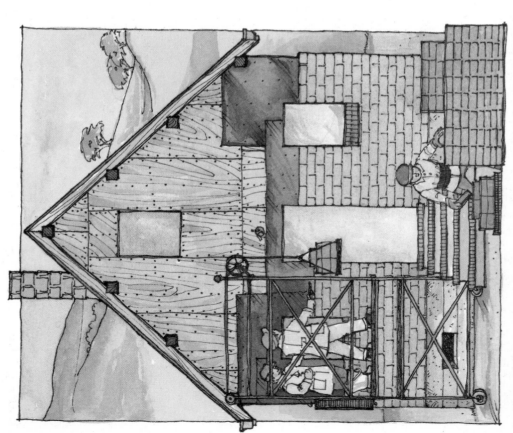

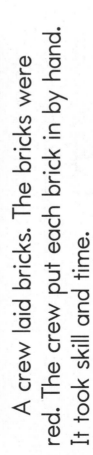

A crew laid bricks. The bricks were red. The crew put each brick in by hand. It took skill and time.

12

241

A week later, Dean and Mom came
back. The hole now had cement walls.
On top, it had four steel beams.

6

Electric wires were added. Wires
were put in walls.
It takes a lot of know-how to get
the wires right.

11

243

"Steel beams will hold up the house," said Mom.

Three weeks later, Dean was back. A team of four carpenters hammered.

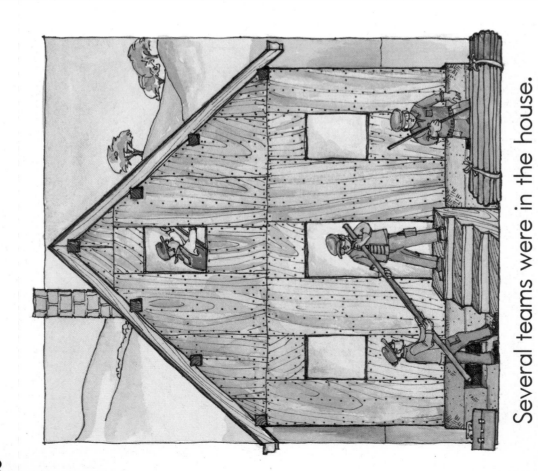

Several teams were in the house. Men put in pipes. Some pipes were for water. Some were for gas. Gas will heat the house.

The frame went up quickly. Dad also came to check the house. Dad pointed. "You will sleep in a bedroom there."

Dean liked seeing the team. He learned a lot.

Dean took a deep breath. He liked smelling fresh wood.

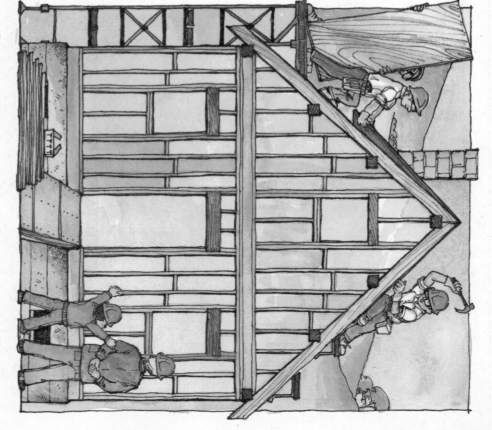

SRA Decodables

Gramps's Pals

by Nancy Tyler
illustrated by Len Ebert

Core Decodable 108

McGraw Hill SRA

Columbus, OH

"My home is filled," said Gramps. "I never feel alone."
A bluebird flew past. Gramps waved. Clare gave Gramps a hug.

16

The McGraw-Hill Companies

Gramps and Clare stood on the porch. "Let's be still and look," said Gramps. Clare did. She saw birds, squirrels, bugs, and a mouse.

246

Clare visited Gramps. His house was old. And Gramps was older than his house. He stayed there with Sweeney, his dog.

3

Gramps sniffed. "Smell a skunk?" he asked.

"Where?" Clare yelled and jumped.

"A skunk sleeps under the steps," said Gramps.

14

Mom and Dad were concerned. Gramps spent much time alone. They visited him every week. They still were afraid he felt lonely.

4

Clare spotted them. "Those are bats. I let them stay for free," said Gramps. Clare's grin grew bigger.

13

248

"Are you lonely, Gramps?" Clare asked. Gramps smiled. "Not much. I'm not really alone," he said.

5

Gramps sat on a swing. He pointed at the house. "See where the roof ends," he said. "See those twin black bumps."

12

Clare brushed Sweeney's back. "You just have Sweeney," she said. Gramps smiled. "Come for a stroll in the yard," he said.

6

Next Gramps stopped by a small pond in his yard. "This is where green frogs greet me every morning," he said.

11

In the yard, Gramps said, "Sweeney and I are not alone. Several pals call this place home."

Gramps pointed to a nest.

7

"This is where gray rabbits hide," Gramps said. "They nibble my plants. They can since they call this yard home."

10

"See the bluebirds in the tree," said Gramps. "Every day I wave to them. And they flap a wing at me."

Clare grinned.

8

Gramps walked in his garden. "These bright flowers are part of my home. So are the butterflies and bees that flutter around."

9

SRA Decodables

Houses

by Maria Johnson
illustrated by Doug Roy

Core Decodable 109

SRA

Columbus, OH

Josh looked out the window. "I see the truth," he thought. "Ruth's nephew has just one house. It has wheels!"

16

253

In September, Josh's phone rang. "Josh, this is Ruth," said a voice. "I am calling from my nephew's house in the street."

Sunshine filled the yard. Josh rested
on his shady porch. It was hot for the
third week in May.

3

"That is his fifth house!" thought Josh.
"Ruth's nephew must be very, very rich."
But Josh still did not say that.

14

At the next house, Ruth checked her mail. "My nephew sent a postcard," she called. "He is in his house on the beach."

In August, Josh brushed his dog's fur. "My nephew sent a photo," said Ruth. "He is in his house in the far north."

257

"His house is on the beach!" Josh thought. "I wish I had a house on the beach."

But he did not say that.

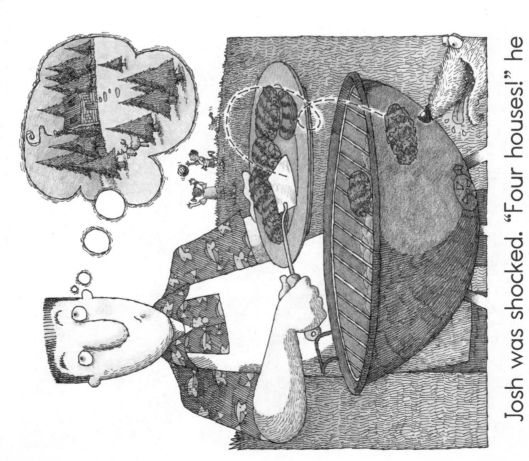

Josh was shocked. "Four houses!" he thought. "How can Ruth's nephew own four houses?"

But Josh did not say that.

In early June, Josh painted a bench.
"My nephew wrote me," Ruth said.
"He is in his house at the ranch."

Later, Ruth said, "I got a call from my nephew. He is in his house in the woods. He is searching for birds."

"Wow," thought Josh. "Ruth's nephew has two houses! How did he pay for both?"

But he did not say that.

It was later in the summer. Josh was making lunch for a bunch of pals. He heard a phone ring in Ruth's house.

In late June, Josh cleaned his car.
"I heard from my nephew," Ruth
said. "He is in his house at the river."

8

Now Josh thought, "Ruth's nephew
must be rich. He has three houses."
But Josh did not say that.

9

SRA Decodables

A Summer Home

by Tom Sato
illustrated by Robin Kerr

Core Decodable 110

Mc Graw Hill SRA

Columbus, OH

Later in the summer, Dad placed tin over the rolled-up awning. Birds cannot make a nest there. We can use the awning.

Dad learned!

16

All summer, Dad did not start the motor. And he did not open the awning. New birds were born and grew.

263

Last summer, Dad was thrilled. He had a large new awning! It was green and white. It could shade the backyard porch.

3

I was concerned. Would Dad brush the nest away? He did not. "Now this nest is a home," he said.

14

It was not hard to open the awning. Dad just hit a button. A little motor turned on, and the awning rolled out.

4

On Thursday, we came back. On the porch, Dad heard a bird. He grabbed his ladder.

"A nest with eggs!" he whispered.

13

Early one day, I was on the porch.
The awning was rolled up. I heard a
bird. I looked up.

5

"See," said Dad. "The bird is smart.
It searched for a better place."
The next Sunday we visited a farm.

12

A bird was perched on the rolled-up awning. It had started to make a nest there. I called Dad.

6

Each day, Dad brushed the twigs away. After the third day, the bird stopped. It must have made a nest far away.

11

The bird flew away. In a hurry, Dad grabbed a short ladder. He climbed up it. He looked at the nest.

7

At first, the bird did not learn. Each day it perched on the awning. Each day, it started to make a nest.

10

"So far, this is just twigs," Dad said.
He brushed them away.
"The bird will learn not to make a nest here."

8

I was surprised. Dad could tell.
"Do not be concerned," he said.
"This will not hurt the bird. It will learn."

9

SRA Decodables

The Every Kid Club

by Anne O'Brien
illustrated by Gioia Fiammenghi

Core Decodable 111

McGraw Hill SRA

Columbus, OH

"The Every Kid Club is lots of fun!" shouted Rose.

16

"It's getting crowded!" said Rose. "How about just calling it the Every Kid Club?" Abby crossed out ALL GRADES and painted EVERY KID. Then she painted lots of faces.

ALL EVERY!
FIRST GRADES
~~THREE GIRLS~~ CLUB

Abby and Rose went over to
Nancy's yard to play.

"Hi!" called Abby's little sister.
"Can I come up?"
"Well," said Abby, "we have a club.
It's called the All Grades Club, and you
aren't even in kindergarten!"

4

"Hurry up!" called Nancy.
"We can play in my tree house!"

"Well," said Holly, "how about the All Grades Club?"
Abby crossed out FIRST, added an S, and painted ALL.
Then she painted a sixth face.
"Now we are the All Grades Club!" chuckled Rose.

13

"Wow! What a neat place!" said Abby.
"Let's make a club!" said Rose.
"We can call it the Three Girls Club."

5

"Hi!" called Nancy's big brother, Tom. "Can I climb up?"
"Well," said Nancy, "this is the First Grade Club, and you aren't in first grade."
Tom scowled.

12

Rose got out paints and paper.
Abby painted THREE GIRLS CLUB and three faces on the paper.

"Well," said Nancy, "how about the First Grade Club?"

Abby crossed out GIRLS and painted FIRST GRADE.

Then she painted a fifth face.

"Now we are the First Grade Club!" said Rose.

"Hi!" called Holly. "Can I climb up?"
Nancy said, "We have a club. It's called the Three Girls Club. You would make four."
Holly looked down. She hung her head.

7

"Hi!" called David. "Can I climb up?"
"Well," said Nancy, "this is a club for girls, and you aren't a girl."
David frowned. He kicked the dirt.

10

"Well," said Nancy, "how about just Girls Club?"

Abby crossed out THREE and painted a face.

"Now we are the Girls Club!" shouted Rose.

8

9

SRA Decodables

Brave Tony

by Dennis Fertig

illustrated by Siri Weber Feeney

Core Decodable 112

SRA

McGraw Hill

Columbus, OH

Mr. Bloom saw Tony's book. "I like that brave climber," he said.

He and Tony talked and talked. Brave Tony made a good pal.

16

The McGraw-Hill Companies

2

Tony told him in a nice way. Mr. Bloom smiled and said, "Tony, you are right. I will turn down that light."

15

279

On a hot night, Tony liked his window and blinds open. Then he could feel cool breezes. He could see the moon.

3

"Hi, Tony," said Mister Bloom.

"Hi, Mr. Bloom," said Tony. Then Tony followed his plan. He told Mr. Bloom about the light.

14

Lately, a bright light changed things. It filled Tony's room. He had to shut his blinds. The light came from the next house.

4

The next afternoon, Tony went to Mr. Bloom. Tony carried the book with him. It helped him act bravely.

13

The house was Mr. Bloom's. He was
new on the block. He did not talk much.
He just stood and looked at plants.

5

Tony thought about how the brave
man climbed the peak. That man made a
good plan. Tony would, too.

12

Now Tony was not thinking about Mr. Bloom. Tony was reading a good book. It was about a brave man.

6

A Good Plan

Tony knew what he had to do. He had to talk to Mr. Bloom soon. But Tony felt afraid.

11

The man took a chance. He climbed the highest peak on Earth. The man was brave, but not foolish. He made good plans.

7

When he did, Tony's room was bright. It seemed like his lamp was still on. Tony shook his head. It was too bright!

10

The book was true. The man was real. Tony liked true books. He liked them better than made-up books.

8

Soon Tony flipped his lamp switch. He had to go to sleep. It was hot. Tony opened his blinds and window.

9

SRA Decodables

Camping Out

by William Overturf
illustrated by Carol Heyer

Core Decodable 113

SRA

Columbus, OH

The sun woke Brook up. "I slept well," she said.

Audrey did not say a thing. She was sound asleep at last.

16

The McGraw-Hill Companies

2

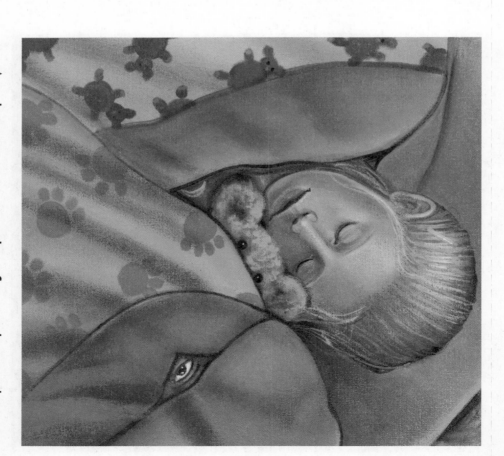

Audrey was awake for a long, long time. She thought she heard a mouse. She thought she heard a shout. And Brook just slept.

15

Plans for a Camp Out

The girls waited all week. On Saturday, they would camp out. They would sleep on the ground in a tent.

Audrey slid down in her sleeping bag. She felt so afraid. She did not even have the power to talk.

"I hope I will not be afraid," said
Brook. "I have never camped before."

"We will be right in town," said
Audrey.

Then Audrey heard a loud howl!
She jumped. Her hand felt the cold,
moist soil. There might be bugs in the
ground!

"And we will be next to my house.
My mom and dad will be around,"
Audrey added. "You will enjoy camping
out."

5

Audrey felt very afraid. What could
she do? Call her mom? Run to the
house?

"I must stay," she frowned.

12

At last, it was Saturday night. Audrey's dad made dinner. He grilled corn in foil. He also made sweet and sour chicken.

6

Audrey heard a sound. Was it a growl? There was more noise. Was an animal prowling around? Brook just slept.

11

At nine, there were no clouds in the dark sky. The girls saw the round moon and a thousand stars.

7

Afraid in the Tent

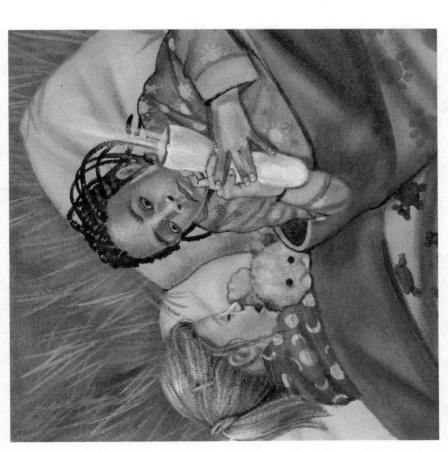

Brook quickly fell asleep. Audrey did not. She felt afraid!

"Being afraid is stupid," she thought. "I am right by my house."

10

Audrey's mom and dad said good night. The girls crawled in the tent.

"Are you afraid, Brook?" asked Audrey.

8

Brook thought about it. She was surprised. She did not feel afraid.

"Wow," said Brook. "I feel fine now."

9

Andy was an artist. His glass made rainbows dance in rooms. It also made him brave.

16

SRA Decodables

Andy Lee

by Jennifer Jacobson
illustrated by Jon Agee

Core Decodable 114

 SRA

Columbus, OH

Andy turned around. The chair was not knocking, and drapes were not swaying. The tablecloth was not floating. The hat was not tipping. It was not dark and scary in there. Rainbows danced in the room.

Andy Lee the Timid

Andy Lee was a timid man. He was also an artist and made stained glass windows. His glass made rainbows dance in rooms.

3

Andy felt a breeze. He found a broken window. He put in the new window. It fit perfectly.

14

One day, Andy made a window pane for an inn. He took the window pane to an inn that was far away. Timid Andy walked and walked.

Timid Andy walked in. It was dark and scary. A chair was knocking, drapes were swaying, a tablecloth was floating, and a hat was tipping.

12

Andy came to the town where
the inn was. Down the street ran
a maid.

"Turn back!" she cried. "Do not
go! A chair is knocking. Drapes
are swaying. It's dark and awful
in that inn!"

"Stay with me," whispered
timid Andy.

6

11

Andy Lee the Brave

Andy, the maid, and the cook stood at the entrance. Out ran an innkeeper.

"Turn back!" she cried. "A chair is knocking. Drapes are swaying. A tablecloth is floating, and a hat is tipping. It's dark and scary in here!"

"But what about the window?" asked Andy. "I am a timid man, but this is my best window ever. I will still put in my window."

10

Andy and the maid came to a gate.

Out ran a cook waving a spoon.

"Turn back!" cried the cook. "A chair is knocking. Drapes are swaying. A tablecloth is floating. It's dark and scary in there!"

"Stay with me," whispered timid Andy.

8

9

SRA Decodables

How the Rabbit Caught the Tiger

by Patricia Griffith
illustrated by Pat Doyle

Core Decodable 115

 SRA

Columbus, OH

The rabbit giggled and scampered away. He had tricked a mighty tiger!

301

SRAonline.com

Mc Graw Hill **SRA**

Copyright © 2008 by SRA/McGraw-Hill.

Printed in the United States of America.

Send all inquiries to this address:
SRA/McGraw-Hill
4400 Easton Commons
Columbus, OH 43219

The McGraw-Hill Companies

The tiger tugged and tugged, but his tail did not come out. It was frozen in solid ice!

"I'm going to get you, little rabbit!" roared the tiger. But he could not budge at all.

The Rabbit and the Tiger

One winter's eve, a mighty and hungry tiger trapped a tiny rabbit.

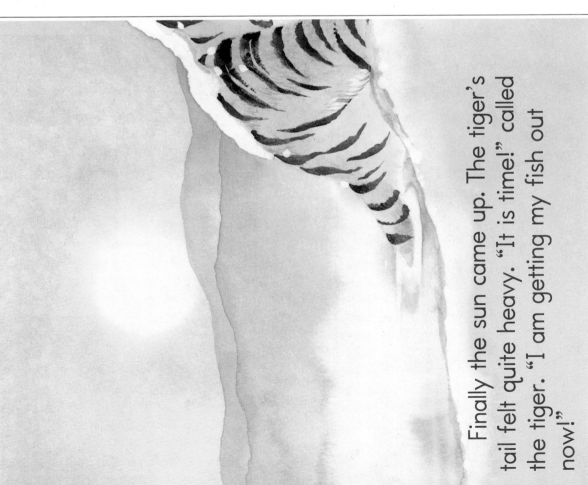

Finally the sun came up. The tiger's tail felt quite heavy. "It is time!" called the tiger. "I am getting my fish out now!"

"Do not eat me!" cried the rabbit. "I am too small to make a good meal. If you let me go, I will show you how to catch all the fish you can eat."

The greedy tiger waited longer. It grew colder and colder. His tail grew heavier.

The tiger was greedy. His hunger was bigger than his brain. "Show me now, or I will eat you, little rabbit!" he roared. Then he let the rabbit go.

5

"No!" cried the rabbit. "If you wait until morning, you will have more fish to eat!"

12

The rabbit led the tiger down to a river. The rabbit told the tiger, "Put your tail in the water."

6

11

307

7

"Now wait all night. Fish will grab your tail. Soon your tail will grow heavy. Then you can take it out and eat all the fish!"

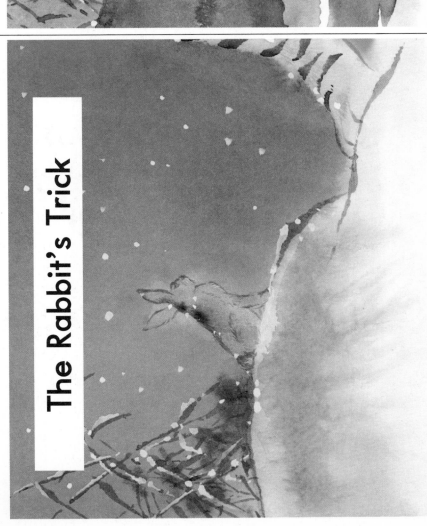

The Rabbit's Trick

"Is your tail getting heavy?" called the rabbit.

"Yes!" replied the tiger. "I must be catching lots of fish! Do you think I ought to take my tail out now?"

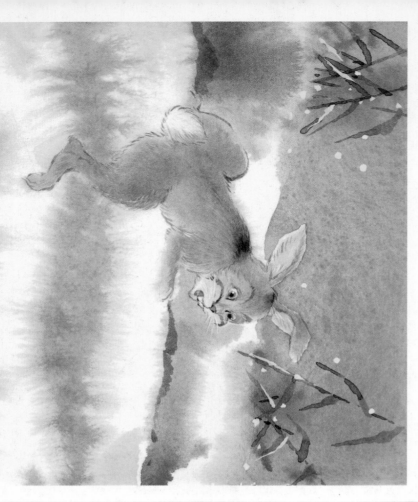

"I'll stay close by," whispered the rabbit.

"I will let you know when you have caught plenty of fish."

The rabbit climbed up the riverbank and sat down across from the tiger.

8

The tiger put his tail into the river. He waited and waited. It grew cold and dark.

9